INTEROCEPTION
HOW I FEEL

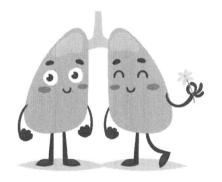

All body clip art graphics used with permission from Teacher's Clipart.

Clip art of children, toilet, and sensory used with permission of Scrappin Doodles.

Publishing and Design Services: MartinPublishingServices.com

INTEROCEPTION
HOW I FEEL

SENSING MY WORLD FROM THE
INSIDEOUT

 CARA N. KOSCINSKI, MOT, OTR/L

CONTENTS

INTRODUCTION

Interoception is quickly becoming the new "buzz word." The information in this book will empower you to understand *WHAT* it is and *HOW* to help yourself, students, and children to get in tune with body signals. In recent years, terms such as *mindfulness*, *body scanning*, and *self-regulation* have grown in popularity among the general population. Yoga and meditation migrated to the mainstream. Further, we are realizing that interaction with nature is critical to human development and use of electronic devices is causing a lack of functional skill development in our children.

Understanding how stress and daily life affect your brain and body can greatly improve both your physical and mental health.

Many research studies prove the benefits of deep breathing and living in the moment, as well as the negative impact of stress hormones. Check out the resource pages at the end of this book for links to many wonderful studies and websites you'll want to add to your library. Throughout this book there are wonderful activities designed to increase interoceptive awareness.

To study interoception, we must discuss sensory processing overall. I've been an OT for over twenty years, and the leaps and bounds of sensory research have drastically improved the impact that therapists make on their clients. More therapists (myself included) are seeking doctorate degrees in the field of occupational therapy, and evidence-based practice continues to evolve and grow. For more information and in-depth explanation about the sensory system, including tips for helping children with struggles in daily self-care and behavior issues, please read my book, *The Parent's Guide to Occupational Therapy for Autism & Special Needs* (Jessica Kingsley Publishers).

The "master" book that psychiatrists and mental health professionals use to diagnose those who live with mental health disorders is called *The Diagnostic and Statistical Manual of Mental Disorders*, or *DSM*. The book, currently in its fifth edition, exists for the purpose of listing all recognized disorders so that a person's insurance and medical record can be coded for consistency. For example, autism spectrum disorder is code 299.0. The code is placed on medical charts, insurance paperwork, billing, etc. When a child receives a diagnosis of autism, the specific criteria used to describe the autism category are always the same. In this way there is consistency among doctors and mental health facilities.

The problem is that sensory processing disorder is NOT listed in the most current edition of the *DSM* (2013). Those of us who live with sensory processing disorder understand the condition is quite real, but there is no diagnosis code for it. However, in the *DSM*, sensory concerns are listed as criteria for autism as follows:

"Hyper- or hypo-reactivity to sensory input or unusual interests in sensory aspects of the environment (e.g., apparent indifference to pain/temperature, adverse response to specific sounds or textures, excessive smelling or touching of objects, visual fascination with lights or movement)." Remember that not everyone with autism has sensory processing disorder and not everyone with sensory processing disorder has autism. In fact, many people with ADD/ADHD, mitochondrial disease, fibromyalgia, and other medical conditions experience sensory integrative problems. Did you know that many 'neuro-typical' individuals experience difficulties processing sensory information too?

The focus of this book is on interoception, but it is critical to list the other sensory areas. Most people are aware that humans have five sensory systems: sight, smell, taste, touch, and hearing. Through research and in-depth studies about the human body, senses such as proprioception and vestibular awareness and now, interoceptive awareness are being understood. Scientists now realize there are additional senses used by our body to improve function and detect our surroundings. Let's discuss the lesser-known senses.

The *tactile system* as defined by the STAR Institute for Sensory Processing Disorder (SPDStar.org):

> "The tactile system is responsible for processing touch information from the body. The body sends tactile information to the somatosensory cortex through neural pathways to the spinal cord, the brain stem, and the thalamus. The primary somatosensory cortex is the primary receptive area for touch sensations and is located in the postcentral gyrus, a prominent structure in the parietal lobe of the human brain. Due to

its many connections to other brain areas, the somatosensory cortex is the part of the nervous system that integrates touch, pressure, temperature, and pain."

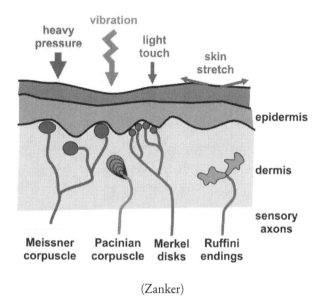

(Zanker)

Our tactile system involves much more than touch. Receptors embedded in our skin help us to detect input that warns us of danger. Remember, our body's main focus is keeping safe and away from potentially dangerous threats. When we place a weighted blanket onto our student, the tactile system is stimulated as we feel the heavy pressure on our body (Koscinski, 2017).

Proprioception allows us to know where our body is positioned in space. Muscles, joints, and ligaments have receptors (muscle spindles and Golgi bodies are examples) that let us know our position. Additionally, they give information about movement, stretch, pain, and more. The brain uses this information to send commands back to the muscles to make adjustments in movement. Both the cerebrum and cerebellum in the brain are used in this process. Have you ever danced to the song, *YMCA?* The movements you are completing depend on accurate position sense as you form the letters with your arms.

The proprioceptive system cannot work alone; it coordinates with the vestibular system. For example, during a neurological examination the doctor asks a patient to close his eyes and use his index finger to touch his nose. This task should be able to be done with ease. We automatically know our position in space and can successfully complete the task without looking. Well-functioning vestibular and proprioceptive systems keep you upright and prevent you from falling when your eyes are closed.

Your vestibular system's job is to detect the position and movement of the head and body in space. Movement in any direction, including linear (forward and backward) and angular (diagonal and tilting), is detected. Our eyes adjust to our movements so we can maintain focus even though we're moving. We perceive our body's orientation (the position we are in) and have control of our posture and balance.

Proprioception is much more than knowing where we are in space; it has wonderful functional abilities. It is required for fine and gross motor movement and for understanding where our body is in relation to someone else's space. When lining up for a fire drill, most of us do not need to bump into the person next to us to determine our position. I recommend using a hula hoop with your student to give a visual reminder of personal space. Another option is to ask your child to stretch arms out to the side and avoid touch within that radius.

Vestibular input comes from receptors in our inner ear. Balance, our position in space and against gravity, and body movements that help keep us upright involve vestibular input. Our entire body—even our eyes—are included!

Here's more information about the vestibular system from the Star Institute:

> "This sensory system has a broad influence in many parts of the brain projecting to:
>
> - The cerebellum (to affect movements of the head, eyes, and posture);
> - Cranial nerves III, IV, and VI (to permit the eyes to fix on a moving object while staying in focus);
> - Reticular formation (to signal how to adjust circulation and breathing when the body assumes a new position);
> - Spinal cord (to allow quick reflex reactions related to balancing); and
> - Thalamus (to control head and body motor responses)."

Let's review the basics. The sensory system involves not only the actual receptors in the skin and body, but also the processing and response formed by the brain. Our response depends partly on our past experiences. When we have experienced a negative situation in the past, we are more likely to worry when we are faced with a similar situation. Our body's natural response is to protect ourselves from potential threats and danger. Stress is our body's response to the threat. Anxiety is our reaction to the stress.

This is why a child who perceives a loud noise as dangerous is afraid of the *possibility* of the noise when they are in the same room with the source (e.g., a dog or fire alarm). When a child looks at the fire alarm, an actual release of stress hormones can occur, causing a potential meltdown. We can use social stories and relaxation techniques to assist children through difficult times. In this book, we are going to learn body scanning as an additional way to help our children.

It is also critically important to remember that some children are HYPER-RESPONSIVE; they show big responses to small bits of sensory information. Others are HYPO-RESPONSIVE; they do not respond enough or respond less than expected. Still others fall into the MIXED category; their response fluctuates depending on the system or their body. The majority of children with whom therapists work have mixed responses in different areas. For example, they may make loud noises with their mouths, but they are afraid of noises in their environment. Even my own children are walking contradictions, showing different sensory sensitivities at different times and/or locations.

I encourage my readers to take an ACEs (Adverse Childhood Experiences) survey. The original study was a part of the CDC-Kaiser Permanente's investigation of child abuse and neglect and its later effects on things such as health and well-being. There is more information about the ACEs survey in the activity sheets download included with this book (https://www.pocketot.com/interoceptionbook). If you would like to take the ACEs survey, you can find it here: https://www.npr.org/sections/health-shots/2015/03/02/387007941/take-the-ace-quiz-and-learn-what-it-does-and-doesnt-mean.

Postural Concerns

Postural concerns are important to consider as well. Have you ever seen a child who simply cannot sit up in a chair OR is literally falling out of her chair when she's at her desk? That child may have difficulty "knowing" where her body is in space, not be able to "adjust her posture" against gravity, be afraid of falling out of the chair, or feel as though she is falling out of the chair.

Motor planning, also called *praxis*, depends on efficient sensory processing. When we want to reach for a hairbrush, our body forms a plan for movement. First, we decide what to do. Then we form a plan, and finally, we carry out (execute) that plan. The entire process depends on our knowledge of past experiences and the senses we feel. Remember that our body uses proprioceptive, vestibular, and other information to adjust and synchronize our body's movement. We can also complete a brand-new task by consciously attending to it and then responding to the environment and past experiences to guide us. Many children with sensory processing difficulties demonstrate poor balance, poor awareness of their body, and clumsiness.

Let's get to **INTEROCEPTION**.... what makes me, ME? What makes you, YOU? Hungry, thirsty, excited, itchy, irritable, sleepy, angry—these are all examples of how a person may be feeling at a given time. The awareness of the inside of your body, including heart rate and breathing, combined with an awareness of emotion defines interoceptive awareness. New research has shown that there is a definite link between interoceptive awareness and emotions as they relate to overall regulation, complex thinking, and sense of self. Additionally, there are studies that suggest that the insula (like other brain areas) demonstrates neuroplasticity, and that we can indeed "practice" awareness! (Dunn et al.; Sze et. al; Kirk et al.; Critchley et al.; and Lazar et al.).

We know that practicing any skill builds connections. It is exciting that the same is true for practicing interoceptive awareness. I know you've heard of "use it or lose it." Let's go further and confirm that the brain that *fires* together—*wires* together! That's right, the more we use connections, the stronger they become; the ones we use less often weaken. As children grow and develop from infancy to adulthood, the brain cuts out connections (synapses) that it does not need or use. This process is called "synaptic pruning." Recent studies have shown that adults can learn and form new brain pathways.

Did you know (according to a scientist named Jean Piaget) that it takes a baby at least six months to a year to differentiate themselves from others—especially their mothers?

"Awareness of one's body is intimately linked to self-identity, the sense of being 'me.' A key question is how the brain integrates different sensory signals from the body to produce the experience of this body as mine, known as sense of body-ownership. Converging evidence suggests that the integration of exteroceptive signals related to the body, such as vision and touch, produces or even alters the sense of body-ownership. However, multisensory integration conveys information about the body as perceived from the outside, and hence, represents only one channel of information available for self-awareness. Interoception, defined here as the sense of the physiological condition of the body, is a ubiquitous information channel used to represent one's body from within. While the effects of exteroception on the physiological regulation of the body have been recently documented, little is known on whether interoceptive awareness may influence exteroceptive representations of one's body. We, therefore, sought to understand the interaction between interoceptive and exteroceptive awareness of the body using interoceptive sensitivity measures and bodily illusions" (Lab of Action and Body, Royal Holloway, University of London. Accessed 11/7/16).

What does this article mean? Extroception (according to the Merriam-Webster dictionary) means "outside stimuli." This is something that happens TO our body from the outside. We seek to determine how our past experiences and feelings cause us to interact with our environment and how it affects us, so our health and bodily well-being are impacted by interoception. It is for this reason that we need to explore the therapeutic benefits of teaching our children HOW to interact with and know ABOUT their bodies.

Homeostasis

"Interoception refers to the sensing of internal bodily changes. Interoception interacts with cognition and emotion, making measurement of individual differences in interoceptive ability broadly relevant to neuropsychology" (Garfinkel et al., 2015).

We survive daily by regulating basic body functions designed to maintain life. In Greek, the word *homeostasis* means "same" or "steady." It was described at length by a physician named Walter Cannon in the 1930s. Dr. Cannon's book called *The Wisdom of the Body* is a wonderful book that I keep in my library. Humans operate on the "survival of the fittest" principle. From the cellular level to the body system level, a healthy organism must work in synthesis for stability internally in an externally changing setting.

We know that both physical and psychosocial stressors placed on our body cause reactions of various types. Some of the obvious body systems requiring regulation include:

- temperature
- blood sugar
- blood oxygen level
- hunger
- thirst
- salt (salinity) levels
- protein
- evacuation of waste (urine and feces), as well as metabolic waste

UNDERSTAND THE INSULA

Johann Christian Riel (1759–1813) has a great deal to do with our discussion of interoception. He was the first doctor to name "psychiatry," as he felt there needed to be a specialist group of physicians who worked specifically with patients who had mental illness. The book in which he first wrote about psychiatry is entitled *Rhapsodieen über die Anwendung der psychischen Curmethode auf Geisteszerrüttungen (Rhapsodies on the Application of Psychic Treatment Methods to Mental Disturbances).*

In his 2007 essay entitled "Psychiatry's 200th birthday," Andreas Marneros stated:

> "Many of his arguments are key to our current thinking about psychiatry. He discussed its fundamental aspects and also pleaded for the rights of mental patients. Riel described psychotherapy as an essential treatment for mental and somatic diseases and as having equivalence with pharmacological and surgical methods. He addressed issues of counteracting stigma and argued for humane mental hospitals and a greater responsibility of society and government for their mentally ill citizens."

As I prepared for this book, I was reminded of the importance of understanding our own mental health and learning how to empower ourselves with helpful techniques that can be used regularly. One of the foundations of occupational therapy is our work in mental health. Early OTs focused on reintegration of patients with mental health issues from institutions into the community. Our profession strives to help people engage in meaningful roles in multiple settings across the lifespan. When thinking about interoceptive awareness, it's important to remember that as therapists, we are called to help our patients learn techniques that assist with independence. Working on the ability to understand our own bodies and integration with our environment is key to optimal functional outcomes.

In his work, Riel described the insula. Our understanding of this critical brain structure is growing by leaps and bounds. In fact, it was a little-known portion of the brain even a few decades ago. The insula is tucked away in the lateral sulcus—the region of the brain that separates the frontal, parietal, and temporal lobes of the brain.

New and exciting research by neuroscientist Antonio Damasio shows that our emotions contribute to decision making. One of Dr. Damasio's discussions (TED Talk 2011) on consciousness can be viewed here: https://www.ted.com/talks/antonio_damasio_the_quest_to_understand_consciousness.

In his TED Talk, Dr. Damasio reports, "We generate brain maps of the body's interior and use them as the reference for all the other maps." When considering his views on internal regulation, we understand that homeostasis means we unconsciously regulate our internal body state, so it does not fluctuate greatly. If it does, we may be in a state of disease or even death. Heart rate, salinity, temperature, and regulation of waste from food and metabolism are examples. We must regularly maintain our bodies by monitoring our bloodwork, urinalysis, blood pressure, oxygen levels, etc. Further, we constantly create mental images based on our experiences and refer to them when creating new memories. Dr. Damasio's extensive research as a well-respected neurologist can help us to understand interoception.

The insular cortex is responsible for mapping somatic states. *Soma* means "body" in Latin, so when we use the word *somatic*, we are referring to the body. Further, the Mayo Clinic describes somatic symptom disorder as "having significant focus on physical symptoms—such as pain and fatigue—to the point where it causes major emotional distress and problems functioning." Researchers found that the insular cortex provides an emotional context for our physiological experiences. We feel pain and understand that it is not a pleasant experience. The insular cortex helps us to automatically know that we are each our own separate beings and not a part of the park bench on which we are sitting. We automatically know when we are hungry or thirsty, need to use the toilet, or need to stop a bad habit. We also experience those "gut feelings" that guide us along life's journey. Additionally, it helps us to understand our own and others' emotions and helps us with social skills.

The insular cortex also has direct connections to the amygdala and hippocampus of the limbic system. That system helps us to make new memories; react emotionally to our environment; and maintain our alertness, sleep/wake cycles, and other areas of homeostasis. It's easy to see the invaluable connection between our body's survival and our emotions when considering the insular cortex and limbic system's intimate connection.

Research by Stephani et al. in 2011 found, "A relatively high density of electrode contacts enabled us to delineate several functionally distinct areas within the insula. We found somatosensory symptoms to be restricted to the posterior insula and a subgroup of warmth or painful sensations in the dorsal posterior insula." Additionally, Dr. Martin Paulus and his team at the Laureate Institute for Brain Research work on research about the insula. An article by Farb et al. (2015) states:

> "From a computational perspective, the simulation map is the ongoing selection of encoded body states into a working memory buffer that serves as the best approximation of the body's current state as predicted by these prior states. The simulation map is layered, with lowest layers being closest to raw sensory afferents from the body, and higher layers representing the aggregation of information at these lower layers into representations that may be accessible to consciousness. As such, the simulation map affords executive brain areas with relatively stable sensory representations from which to interpret experience and coordinate responses."

The interesting thing about interoception is that it guides our responses for survival.

Possible Barriers to Working with Interoception

As I researched for this book, I frequently bumped into skeptics who don't "believe in" our ability to have true body awareness and to practice some form of control over our body. For example, some believe ideas in traditional Eastern medicine are hokey or do not relate to our Western medical model. Further, even though the practice of mindfulness or meditation has existed for ages, it is still seen as a fad or phase existing in popular culture. I end each of my conferences with the statement, "Do the BEST that you can with what you know and when you learn better—do better!" After all, the interventions I'll discuss in this book are low-cost or free, so why not try something that might work to improve your child's life? Welcome skeptics!

Connections

Children learn through play and gain awareness of their body as they explore their surroundings. Consider the infant who quickly learns to hold his head up against gravity. When he is successful, he repeats the behavior. When he unsuccessfully completes the task, he is less likely to repeat it and has learned, "I will not do THAT again." Natural consequences are outcomes that are a result of someone's behavior. They are not planned out. Here are some examples:

> Jennifer does not like what is served for dinner. She chooses not to eat, and her parents allow her to make her choice. She feels hungry later in the evening. Jennifer quickly learns that if she chooses not to eat dinner, she will experience hunger. If she is not given any more food for the evening, she will be hungry and learn the consequence of her choice.

> Michael is one year old and is beginning to walk. He learns that holding onto the coffee table allows him to walk faster and fall less. He is likely to repeat this behavior.

> John chooses to watch football on Monday night and does not study his spelling words. He fails his test as a result.

The problem with children who have decreased interoceptive awareness is that they may not feel the physical and psychological cues such as hunger, thirst, failure, and stress.

Therapists understand that the way our body *feels* has a direct link to our well-being and condition. There is huge therapeutic value in this concept as we teach children to use their body to improve overall function and well-being. For instance, depression affects not only mood but also overall physical status.

Those who suffer from depression also commonly experience changes in appetite, fatigue, and pain. It is well known among medical professionals and pharmacists that responses to pain and depression share a neurologic pathway. Response to painful stimuli is moderated in the brain by serotonin and norepinephrine, which also affect mood. My husband, who has a clinical doctorate in pharmacy, states that "pain is regulated by the mu receptors and the method of treatment for depression is through SSRI (Selective Serotonin Re-Uptake Inhibitors). Medications such as Cymbalta (duloxetine) inhibit the re-uptake of serotonin and norepinephrine and clinical uses include treatment of major depressive disorder as well as diabetic peripheral neuropathic pain" (Brant Koscinski, PharmD. January 2018 interview).

What about STRESS? Research has shown that stress hijacks the amygdala in our body. This means that when a human is stressed, learning **STOPS**! The implications for our children who have special needs, feel great discomfort due to anxiety, or experience great worry are huge. Their learning might be impaired due to a chemical reaction over which they have no control.

Here's an excerpt from Jean Soyke, a certified teacher

specializing in math and curriculum development for Demme Learning:

> "Neuroscientists have discovered that learning takes place as three parts of the brain interact: the amygdala, which responds to emotion; the hippocampus, which moves experiences to long-term memory; and the cerebral cortex, where information is stored. In the ideal learning experience, the student feels confident and engaged. The pleasant atmosphere and novelty of the material relaxes the amygdala and allows the hippocampus to begin transmitting the new information to the cerebral cortex. In a stressful situation, however, brain function radically changes. The amygdala becomes over-stimulated and blocks access to the hippocampus; in addition, cortisol (a hormone released when a person is under stress) attaches itself to the hippocampus, preventing it from functioning. Thus, the information can't get to the cerebral cortex for long-term storage. If you think back to a particularly stressful situation in your own life, you probably can recall the feeling of not being able to think clearly and not knowing what to do— the result of the amygdala overreacting, and the hippocampus being repressed" (http://www. edudemic.com/stress-affects-brain-learning/ Accessed 11/6/16).

A brief discussion about our nervous system is in order. As I write this book, I'm engaging in one of my favorite hobbies:

attending a neurology course. I feel it is critical to enhance my own learning to better assist my clients and train therapists. Our brain can form pathways throughout our lives, and scientists continue to utilize functional MRI testing to show real-time brain function. Imagine what advances may be coming soon. The sympathetic nervous system serves to accelerate the heart rate, constrict blood vessels, and stimulate sweat glands in response to a perceived threat. According to Dr. Peggy Mason at the University of Chicago, our sympathetic nervous system (located in the thoracic spinal cord) gives us fight, flight, flee in response to stress and this system releases those hormones that essentially hijack our body as we seek safety. These are primal responses, but our experiences actually remake memories since our emotions are great facilitators of memories. In cases of Post-Traumatic Stress Disorder (PTSD), triggers occur that bring about physiological stress in a current situation that we remember from a previous stressful event.

Located in the sacral spinal cord, our parasympathetic nervous system elicits rest and digest processes. Recovery and sleep are necessary for our body to repair itself and absorb nutrients passing through our digestive system. We have two systems that control our body so that we can remain in a state of regulation from moment to moment. However, this changes constantly. I compare it to the weather. Our emotional and regulatory state shifts both predictably and unpredictably. In fact, our emotions are the true backdrop for our daily life experiences. Our perception of the world around us influences how we respond to demands and determines our ultimate regulation and mental presence for learning. Remember, the weather is fickle and so are we!

So what affects us? The current state of our body, both physically and psychologically. However, when we are asked to focus on demands of work, family, and school, we may be forced to ignore how our body truly feels in order to perform functions and tasks. Some of us have developed skills with which to ignore and suppress our interoceptive information, but others— specifically those with sensory processing disorder and/or those who experience sudden onset of pain or physical conditions— may not be able to suppress such information, and thus behavior is affected. REMEMBER THAT OUR BEHAVIOR IS COMMUNICATION!

This weekend I lost my diamond wedding ring. I put it on the counter to peel potatoes; an hour later I realized it was missing. Unfortunately, it was during my son's birthday party. The guests and I tore through trash and crawled on hands and knees searching for it. My sweet husband dismantled the kitchen sink searching for the ring. During that hour, I do not remember what my son and his buddies were talking about or what presents he opened. My entire brain was hijacked by my stress hormones. We call this "fight or flight," and therapists know that during times of great stress, we DO NOT TEACH new skills. Our specific goal is SAFETY. This means that during a sensory meltdown, our sole purpose is to ensure the SAFETY of the child—not to teach a lesson or to discuss what went wrong. (For more information on behavior and meltdowns, please read my full book, *The Parent's Guide to Occupational Therapy for Autism & Special Needs* [Jessica Kingsley Publishers], as it contains a full chapter on the subject plus includes many helpful strategies.) Teachable moments can then occur after our body maintains a calm and regulated state. This takes time as there is no 'off switch' to stop our body from reacting to the chemicals until they are reabsorbed.

Did you know that interoception was first named by a British physiologist in the early 1900s? His name is Sir Charles

Sherrington. According to the *Encyclopedia Britannica*, he studied the nervous function of higher animals. Here's an excerpt:

> "In his classic work, *The Integrative Action of the Nervous System* (1906), he distinguished three main groups of sense organs: exteroceptive, such as those that detect light, sound, odor, and tactile stimuli; interoceptive, exemplified by taste receptors; and proprioceptive or those receptors that detect events occurring in the interior of the organism. He found—especially in his study of the maintenance of posture as a reflex activity—that the muscles' proprioceptors and their nerve trunks play an important role in reflex action, maintaining the animal's upright stance against the force of gravity, despite the removal of the cerebrum and the severing of the tactile sensory nerves of the skin.
>
> "His investigations of nearly every aspect of mammalian nervous function directly influenced the development of brain surgery and the treatment of such nervous disorders as paralysis and atrophy."

I don't know about you, but I'm certainly glad that Sir Sherrington did research! He truly revolutionized brain surgery and neurology as we know it today.

WHERE IS THE CENTER OF INTEROCEPTION?

Our brain depends on effective communication to function smoothly. As we interact with the world around us, we choose what we will pay attention to and what is important to US. Since each of us has had different upbringings, experiences, and value systems, we each attend to different sets of items. But, to pay attention, we need to "feel" balanced. Remember how stress affects us? If we are stressed, we are not paying as much attention to our surroundings as someone who is relaxed and "taking it all in." This is why we need to understand our own body.

The INSULAR CORTEX is the center of interoception. According to the United States Association for Body Psychotherapy (USABP), there is a growing body of evidence and body of work that is increasing our understanding and treatment using body-awareness. So where is the insular cortex? Its two halves reside deep in the brain in the area separating our temporal (side) from our frontal (front) and parietal (top) brain lobes (areas). Neurologists know that the insular cortex takes up less than 2% of the brain's area. Did you know that the insula is deep in the brain and wasn't fully understood and researched because it wasn't associated with "higher level" brain functions?

The scientist Antonio Damasio discussed our ability to "mark" information we perceive (realize and gain) from the world around us so it has a certain value to our individual functioning. In fact, this helps us to make decisions. Damasio discusses that when we are conscious, we ask ourselves those questions such as, "What am I looking at and how do I feel about it?" We are aware of both our setting and feelings.

So interoception is CRITICAL for SELF-CARE and body REGULATION. This means that interoception may also affect our self-esteem, sense of well-being, and understanding of who WE are. I found the following written by Dr. Simon Moss in his article for Scio Tests:

> "The insular cortex seems to be intimately involved in decision making, especially when the outcomes are uncertain (e.g., Preuschoff, Quartz, & Bossaerts, 2008). That is, individuals often need to decide which of several alternatives to pursue. Occasionally, some of these options could potentially elicit a host of aversive outcomes. When individuals anticipate the possibility of potential adversities, the insular cortex seems to become especially activated (e.g., Critchley, Mathias, & Dolan, 2001 & Smith, Mitchell, Hardin, Jazbec, Fridberg, Blair, & Ernst, 2009). Indeed, anticipation of negative stimuli is regarded as one of the key functions of the insular cortex" (e.g., Seymour, Singer, & Dolan, 2007).

Perhaps because of this anticipation of negative events, activation of the insula is correlated with risk aversion (e.g., Kuhnen & Knutzon, 2005 & Paulus, Rogalsky, Simmons, Feinstein, & Stein, 2003). Indeed, after lesions of the insular cortex, individuals prefer more risky options in gambling tasks—that is, options in which the outcomes are less certain (Clark, Bechara, Damasio, Aitken, Sahakian, & Robbins, 2008). Presumably, when this region is activated, individuals become more sensitive to adverse possibilities, sometimes called a sensitivity to punishment. Risky alternatives, in which adversities are possible, thus seem less appealing.

"In humans, functional neuroimaging studies implicate the anterior insula and pre/subgenual ACC (anterior cingulate cortex) in emotional processes, the mid-posterior insula with awareness and interoception, and the MCC (mid-cingulate cortex) with environmental monitoring, response selection, and skeletomotor body orientation" (Taylor et al., 2009).

The insula helps us to realize emotions, pain, fear, excitement, sadness, or anger. As a part of the limbic system, it allows us to feel those basic human drives such as sexual desire, hunger, and thirst. So we are subjective beings with our own desires, drives, wants, and needs. One more point . . . our perception of something as good versus bad is also subjective and depends on our own feelings.

What does this all mean? What we direct our attention to depends on what's important to us at the time. Sometimes we are conscious of this, but most often we are not. Think about a child with attention deficit disorder. His attention moves from item to item in a busy classroom. He hears the clock tick, another student's pencil tapping, and the teacher speaking; he feels his stomach growling with anticipation of lunch and looks forward to his baseball game later in the day.

Here's a list of possible information a person may attend to:

- tactile (feeling of clothing, pressure, types of touch)

- proprioceptive and vestibular (balance, coordination of body for posture, fine and gross motor coordination)
- cognitive (attention to task, worry, love, anxiety, happiness, sadness, emotions, sense of time, sadness, flexible thinking)
- bladder, bowels, sexual arousal, orgasm, thirst, pain, temperature, swallowing
- rule following, impulsive urges, motivation, ability to notice and empathize with emotions of others, self-awareness

We don't only feel and perceive the information above; we also are driven to act or move or to "fix" or solve the situation. For example, if my body has taken in too much sodium, on a physiological level it requires water to maintain cellular function. First, I must realize the urge and then act to stand up, move to the sink, get a cup, and prepare the water for drinking.

As an occupational therapist, I realize there are MANY steps in the process of completing even a simple task. When faced with any number of psychological and physiological conditions, we may struggle with any portion of the task. You may now begin to realize how very difficult our interoceptive system is. After a stroke, a person might not be able to walk to the sink or physically turn on the water. A child with sensory processing difficulties might not feel thirsty at all. Now consider that our emotional system responds to our physical body's state. A child with a behavior issue may just be thirsty and not feel the sensation. His actions of crankiness, showing bad behavior, crying, or fussing may all be physically driven.

TRAUMA AND ITS EFFECT ON OUR ENTIRE BODY

As a trained trauma-informed therapist, my mission is to view a person's behavior, actions, and emotional status through a more sensitive "lens." I'm often asked, "What does 'trauma-informed' mean?" When we experience a stressful event, our midbrain is "triggered" and produces a stress hormone called cortisol. This enables us to respond when our body is threatened—we can fight back, flee the area to get to safety, or freeze. The problem is that when we feel threatened by sensory experiences and cannot seek help or even find the words to express our fears, we learn to accept and live with the stress. Often, the frequent release of cortisol leads to chronic stress which can harm our bodies and brains.

While there are many models for working with those who experience trauma, let's discuss the NARM (Neuro Affective Relational Model™). Created by Lawrence Heller, PhD, the model examines the physiology and psychology of developmental trauma.

Five Organizing Developmental Themes

There are five developmental life themes and associated core resources that are essential to our capacity for self-regulation.

They also affect our ability to be present to self and others in the here-and-now:

- Connection—We feel that we belong in the world. We are in touch with our body and our emotions and are capable of consistent connection with others.
- Attunement—Our ability to know what we need and to recognize, reach out for, and take in the abundance that life offers.
- Trust—We have an inherent trust in ourselves and others. We feel safe enough to allow a healthy interdependence with others.
- Autonomy—We can say no and set limits with others. We speak our mind without guilt or fear.
- Love-Sexuality—Our heart is open, and we can integrate a loving relationship with a vital sexuality.

"To the degree that these five basic needs are met, we experience regulation and connection. We feel safe and trusting of our environment, fluid and connected to ourselves and others. We experience a sense of regulation and expansion. To the degree that these basic needs are not met, we develop survival styles to try to manage the disconnection and dysregulation" (Heller).

One of my favorite sayings is, *"our brain uses the past to predict the future."* Why? Remember that our own experiences (good and bad) form memories. What we expect greatly depends on what we remember or create using past experience and information. Each of us has sets of patterns and roadmaps which we use to navigate current situations. They are based on our core beliefs, our past, and our current level of alertness or awareness of our environment.

BRAIN HIERARCHY

Infants are born with reflexive abilities. Their survival depends on them. Babies choke or gag for protection of their airway from dangerous items. Tiny hands reflexively grip (palmar grasp reflex) and baby startles by instinctively raising arms up (Moro reflex) in response to unexpected noise. Each primitive reflex is designed to go dormant after its function is fulfilled. Therapists and neurologists call this *reflex integration*. When our reflexes do NOT develop at all or are incomplete in their integration, impairments may result in our body. Difficulties can range from mild to severe, and may affect many areas including our learning, emotions, behavior, and overall development.

In summary, our brains are designed to develop along a specific hierarchy or level. So, when looking at brain dysfunction, doctors often look to reflexes to "speak" for our brain. For example, a doctor uses his hammer during your physical exam to elicit a knee-jerk reaction. If the reaction is NOT present, a problem may exist. Here's another example: A grown adult fell and hit her head. She should normally not have the Moro startle reflex in response to a sound. If she does, there may be a brain injury.

When children develop, they become more connected to their own world. They learn to think about their actions and how what they do has a consequence or effect. In the book *Pediatric Neuropsychological Intervention* (page 7), Tara Spevaek states:

"*Primary projection areas* serve as a direct inter-
face by receiving information from sensory input pathways and sending information to motor
output pathways. Each primary projection area
possesses a unique type of data. Specifically, the
primary projection areas in the occipital, parietal, and parenteral lobes are specialized for
processing visual, auditory, and body sense/tac-
tile information, respectively, and the primary
projection area of the frontal lobe is specialized
for olfactory and motor information. Next, this
information is sent to the secondary association
areas, where it is converted into symbolic con-
tent. Secondary association areas then transmit
information into tertiary association areas for
higher-level polymodal integration which is necessary for language, attention, memory and executive function" (Spevaek, 2007).

The key is that the information we process in our higher-level
brain is abstract and complex, however, reflexes move through the
brainstem. We do not need rudimentary reflexes to function but
require more complicated brain pathways to form and be utilized
in a frequent manner.

Your brain changes chemically and physically as a new skill is
learned. For example, when someone learns how to play chess or
read a book, their brain adds new connections that did not exist
before. Literal rewiring and development occurs. Studies looking
at our brain as we age show that the brain continues to make
viable connections and new neurons are formed as we learn new
skills.

The awesome brain was designed to be challenged and used

daily. The problem with technology and busy stressful life as we know it is that we rely less on our brain and more on gadgets. It's obvious to many developmentalists, physicians, and therapists that children are not playing outside and exploring nature to learn problem solving and physical play skills. Technology has caused us to become disengaged with the world around us.

Here's a personal story that illustrates this point. My older son and I were invited to speak at the Autism Society of America's 50th Annual Conference. At that time, a popular video game released a "go" version. Our entire family traveled for the first time to New Orleans, Louisiana. There was SO much to explore, yet my own children became infatuated with the game. As we traversed the city's beautiful and historic landscape, we looked back at our children. They were immersed in the game! We watched in awe as they walked past musicians and landmarks we had looked forward to seeing.

Consider your own life. Do you depend on electronic reminders? As you take a walk, do you listen to your earbuds or the sounds of nature? Are you using your phone to text instead of picking up the phone to call your family? We are all used to the conveniences of technology and forget to engage in our world. It's like sleepwalking through our day. In earlier times our focus was on survival, on being aware of the world around us to look for danger. There were no apps for this or that.

Living at a faster pace, focusing on productivity, and keeping up with societal expectations changes our brain in negative ways. The obvious challenge we face as a society is how to reconnect with our bodies. Activities in this book are designed to help. Additionally, mindfulness exercises benefit those with interoception difficulties and those who experience great stress in their lives.

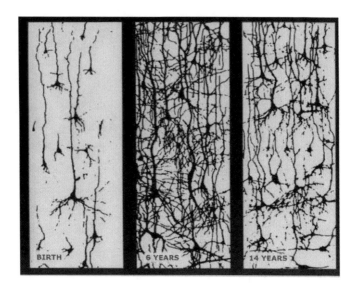

700 New Neural Connections Every Second
Image Source: Conel, JL. The postnatal development of the human
cerebral cortex. Cambridge, Mass: Harvard University Press, 1959

The illustration above shows that infants enter the world with limited neural connections. So a baby born to Chinese parents speaks and learns the customs and language of his parents/caregivers, while a baby born to Spanish parents learns her family's language, traditions, and beliefs. Our brain is literally pre-wired to succeed wherever we enter the world. By six months and at the rate of seven hundred neural connections per second (Conel, 1959), the brain is constantly building connections that are meaningful to and functional for that individual. Scientists used to think that our brains stopped developing at a certain age, but new research has proven that our brains remain plastic (derived from the Greek word *plastos*, meaning molded) throughout our lives.

"[The] organization of brain circuitry is constantly changing as a function of experience. These changes are referred to as brain plasticity, and they are associated with functional changes that include phenomena such as memory, addiction, and recovery of function.

"Recent research has shown that brain plasticity and behavior can be influenced by a myriad of factors, including both pre- and post-natal experience, drugs, hormones, maturation, aging, diet, disease, and stress. Understanding how these factors influence brain organization and function is important not only for understanding both normal and abnormal behavior, but also for designing treatments for behavioral and psychological disorders ranging from addiction to stroke" (Kolb & Whishaw, 1998).

Our body develops along a pre-determined continuum. We often use a pyramid to illustrate both higher-level skills and the foundational skills on which they are based. When thinking of function, consider the level of the skill and look at the skills below it to ensure they are in place. Therapists are specifically trained to analyze tasks and determine which specific skill is used. For example, when a child shows difficulty with handwriting, we need to determine if the problem is with the hand musculature, trouble forming the motor plan, or difficulty supporting her trunk to provide the necessary stability for the arm and hand to function properly. So, using the pyramid illustration (p. 32), how does interoception fit in? Consider whether the child is experiencing stress about how slowly she's writing compared to her peers, as well as the effect on her adrenaline and cortisol. Her heart might be beating too quickly, her breathing may be rapid, and she may be feeling faint or weak. The fact is, we do not routinely check for physiological signs when considering functional difficulties. I challenge all therapists to assess emotional awareness and interoceptive perception during routine evaluations.

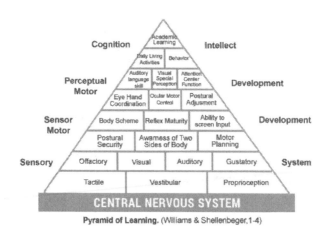

Pyramid of Learning. (Williams & Shellenberger, 1-4)

(Williams & Shellenberger, 1996)

Here's another example: A child with limited verbal skills demonstrates feeding difficulties and refuses to sit and eat with her family at dinner. She is told to sit and eat the food that's on her plate. She becomes agitated and acts out, causing disruption of the mealtime. The family gets frustrated, the child gets upset, and no one wins. Where IS the problem? Could it be the temperature of the food; the odor or taste of the food; difficulty using the feeding utensils; constipation from not having a bowel movement in two days; not feeling hungry; reflux; or a headache from sensory overload at school? The possibilities are endless when we factor in interoception difficulty.

When we consider the pyramids of development, we quickly notice that reflexes are near the bottom. Also note the foundational position of sensory processing. It's evident why children who experience sensory processing disorder experience such great difficulty in many areas of their lives. Without a strong and stable sensory base, our higher brain skills such as language, organization, hand-eye coordination, and other areas cannot function optimally.

Intrinsic and Extrinsic Feedback

One of the most shocking revelations for most families is that posture and the ability to remain upright is not an easy task for children who have disruption in sensory processing, reflexes, and other areas. In fact, when our core muscles do not develop properly, our ability to support ourselves, use our hands for functional tasks, or pay attention and learn can be greatly affected.

Consider this: A student on the playground wants to climb the steps to use the sliding board. He uses sensory and proprioceptive information to determine the position of his arms and legs. He must visually judge the distance his foot needs to move to climb. Vestibular information tells him whether he is off the ground and balancing properly . . . and so on. Let's hypothesize that he misjudges the step and falls a few feet down to the ground. He uses the information to determine if his attempt was a success or failure AND whether he will repeat the task or try something different the next time. Making adjustments based on past experiences is critical as we learn and develop.

Further, ***intrinsic feedback*** involves information we obtain from sensory mechanisms within our bodies. How do we evaluate our actions? When we fall, our body feels pain. When we eat too much, we get a stomach ache. Other times, we can evaluate our actions while we are performing them. An example would be slipping on ice. As you slip, you can shift your weight to keep from falling, or even grab onto your friend walking next to you.

Extrinsic feedback (or augmented feedback) involves information about a task from an outside (external) source. For example, when a teacher uses a visual timer, the students can see the time decreasing. Their own body is not giving the cues, the timer is. Example two: the temperature outside determines how we should cover our bodies with clothing.

Information is received via receptors in the mucous membranes of our various organs to interpret things outside of our bodies. Our nose is equipped with sensory receptors designed to detect smells. Odors evoke powerful feelings since the olfactory lobe is intimately associated with the nerves that detect them. According to Dr. Jane Gaines Lewis, in an article in *Psychology Today* (2015),

> "The answer is likely due to brain anatomy. Incoming smells are first processed by the olfactory bulb, which starts inside the nose and runs along the bottom of the brain. The olfactory bulb has direct connections to two brain areas that are strongly implicated in emotion and memory: the amygdala and hippocampus. Interestingly, visual, auditory (sound), and tactile (touch) information does not pass through these brain areas. This may be why olfaction, more than any other sense, is so successful at triggering emotions and memories."

We move about our day and most likely do not realize how

often we plug our nose or breathe through our mouth so as not to smell a foul odor. Have you ever been in a crowd and someone's perfume smells so strong that you cannot focus on anything else? Imagine how those with sensory hyper-responsivity are affected when a smell such as cologne, cleaning solution, bad breath, or a public restroom is present. Many with olfactory hypersensitivity can smell wet clothing, weather, and other things that are not perceived by others. In fact, my son will not hug my husband when he comes home from work at the hospital since he smells like "hospital." Information about interoception can be detected via nerve endings lining the respiratory and digestive mucous membranes.

Research has been completed confirming that babies can detect the specific smell of their mothers (Romanchick et al.) (Purves et al., 2001). Why is smell such a refined sense from such an early age? If a young baby can detect its mother, he can smell the source of food to nurse. In the same way, we detect smell as it relates to basic needs and safety. The smell of smoke evokes a much different reaction than the smell of vanilla. Vermetten et al. studied smell as it relates to PTSD. Even odors associated with combat can cause "olfactory flashbacks." Consider the implications for those with sensory processing issues. If a smell is associated with a negative experience, then, according to research cited above, the person can experience stress reactions with release of cortisol and adrenaline, causing a fight-or-flight reaction when exposed to triggering smells in a non-dangerous setting! This explains why a child who refuses to urinate in a public restroom may prefer wetting himself to using the toilet.

Smell and Taste

When you have a stuffy nose, you cannot taste your food. The American Academy of Otolaryngology–Head and Neck Surgery states that taste buds exist in the mouth and throat. The system that detects smell and taste is part of our chemical sensing system (chemo sensation).

It's the interaction between taste and smell that determines our true perception of what we are eating. Taste and smell are separate senses with their own receptor organs, yet they are intimately entwined. Tastants, chemicals in foods, are detected by taste buds, which consist of special sensory cells. When stimulated, these cells send signals to specific areas of the brain, which make us conscious of the perception of taste. Similarly, specialized cells in the nose pick up odorants, airborne odor molecules. Odorants stimulate receptor proteins found on hair like cilia at the tips of the sensory cells, a process that initiates a neural response. Ultimately, messages about taste and smell converge, allowing us to detect the flavors of food.

When our sensory processing system is hyper-responsive to smell and taste, strong responses to taste and smell may be present and may cause extreme reactions. In some cases, fight-or-flight responses release hormones that indicate danger, and stress responses begin. If we think about "picky eaters" or "extra-sensitive" individuals as having a TRUE CHEMICAL reaction, we might look at them much differently. In this case, behavior is not the cause, but their actions are chemically driven.

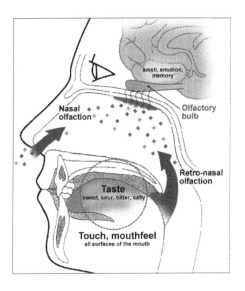

http://enologyinternational.com/psychology.php

Having taken many feeding therapy courses, I know that there are basically four basic tastes: sweet, sour, bitter, and salty. Many patients with whom I work have undergone chemotherapy and radiation treatments. One of the most frustrating complaints is the alteration of taste with aggressive treatments for rapidly growing cancer cells. There can be a physical change in sensation and perception or taste and smell. Boyce and Shone discuss how the aging process affects the two senses. (Boyce & Shone, 2006)

Indeed, there is a much smaller body of work on taste and smell versus other sensory loss (such as vision and learning) in aging patients. However, consider that a primary function of smell is to protect us from danger. The awareness of the pungent smells of a gas leak or a fire burning signal immediate danger and trigger our fight-or-flight responses. As a therapist assisting patients with disease or disorder to return home independently, I know that the ability to perceive and interpret smell can make a huge difference in living situation. Those who cannot detect dangerous odor may be less likely to be able to live independently. Children dealing with sensory processing difficulties often complain of frustration surrounding smell and taste. Their diets may become extremely limited. One of my clients is diagnosed with a severe feeding disorder. He perceives food as rotten. Milk, bread, pasta, or vegetables are described as "rotten" by him. It can be extremely frustrating for him to eat due to the subjective notion that he is given rancid food. Consider perception of odor during a feeding evaluation.

INTEROCEPTION AND EMOTIONS

The world around us is full of information. What we decide is important to us are those pieces of information to which we can apply meaning. Humans' primary interoceptive awareness occurs in the right anterior insula, which provides the basis for subjective feelings of one's emotional awareness.

> "Interoceptive exposure has been validated as an effective component of cognitive behavioral therapy (CBT) for the treatment of panic disorder but has hitherto received little research attention . . . Several interoceptive exposure tasks were particularly effective in reducing pseudo neurological fears. New interoceptive tasks, especially tasks related to cardiorespiratory and dissociative feelings, are needed" (Lee et al., 2006).

As I mentioned earlier, in more than one study, depression is linked to many physical symptoms. Those who suffer from depression commonly experience appetite changes, fatigue, muscle and joint pain, and gastrointestinal problems among many other symptoms. The link between pain and depression appears to be due to a shared neurologic pathway. Response to painful physical stimuli is moderated in the brain by serotonin and norepinephrine, which also affect mood. Patients with neurotransmitter dysregulation may have an imbalance of serotonin and norepinephrine, which may explain the connection between painful physical symptoms and depression. When a patient with depression complains that he or she is feeling physical pain, there may be a chemical reason. Researchers feel that the physiological condition of our body may affect our emotions and perceptions, and vice versa. We all experience feelings based on emotional states. For example, today I'm lamenting the passing of my father a few years ago. I'm feeling melancholy, yet the other members of my family appear excited for a playoff football game on television. They can fully enjoy the game, yet I am unable to respond with excitement since my father loved watching the games with us. I cannot access the emotions of joy and great excitement because my mind exists in a different state. I also seek comfort in one of my favorite activities, eating to "feel better." My contribution to the game is cinnamon rolls with extra icing. As I sit and eat, I feel temporary relief from my sadness. I perceive this day much differently than my family does. Further, I'm experiencing a headache and stomach discomfort along with the psychological manifestations. I encourage readers to think of your own emotions and reactions to sad or traumatizing events.

Carrie Arnold wrote an article for *Scientific American* discussing interoception and a possible relation to distorted body image. Her work involves those with eating disorders. The article encourages readers to become more aware of their internal body processes as a means for improving their own positive images of their body. She encourages mindfulness and yoga as regular activities for people with distorted body images.

Not every child with autism has sensory processing difficulties and not every child with sensory processing difficulties has autism. It is important to remember that many new studies on the brains of people with autism are bringing increased clarity and wonderful information on differences in brain structure. In people with autism, the ability to empathize with others and communicate effectively, as well as the ability to control behavior, can be greatly impaired. Autism disorders are characterized by abnormal functioning in social communication and social interaction across multiple contexts, such as social-emotional reciprocity and nonverbal communicative behaviors used for social interaction, and by restricted, repetitive patterns of behavior, interests, or activities (Diagnostic and Statistical Manual of Mental Disorders DSM-5, American Psychiatric Association).

The Intangibles (Using Your Spidey Sense)

So, what is a "gut feeling" or that feeling when we just know something is right or wrong? In the popular comic book series, Spider Man often felt a sense that something was amiss. Something just didn't feel or look quite right, so he became alarmed. How does this work and is it real?

We use our prior experiences and overall knowledge of right and wrong to quickly evaluate a situation. Through practice, we fine-tune this skill. It is important to understand that our emotions are linked with our ability to maintain the balance necessary to our overall survival. When emotional awareness is "good," we can adapt and react quickly to situations in a variety of settings. However, when we struggle to identify our own feelings and emotions, life can be quite challenging. Many people who demonstrate decreased interoceptive awareness OR poor emotional awareness, show rigidity. Those adults and children who use black-and-white thinking or a specific "rule-based" way of thinking often struggle with the many gray areas in life. Remember that gray areas have no defined set of rules or categories in which to fit. Frustration results as they have not developed and/or practiced trusting their internal awareness of alerts such as feeling "butterflies" in their stomach, hairs standing on end, and intuition.

Children with autism often demonstrate decreased emotional awareness. My younger son often seems rigid and struggles with transitions. He consistently states that he's shy or feels "not brave" when faced with anything out of our typical routine. Many parents report similar struggles with their children. We see low self-esteem, anxiety, depression, self-harm, and overall limited strategies to cope and adjust to the ever-changing world in which they live. When we feel as though we have control of our emotions and overall sense of well-being, we feel better equipped to adapt to our universe. For example, when a current situation is like another one we experienced in the past, we quickly compare it to the previous plan stored in our brain and react accordingly. Through use and practice, we gradually adapt to the emotions we feel and change the plan slightly to fit the new situation. We use our higher brain (cortex) to compare and fine tune our strategy. In fact, we become so efficient that we can process millions or bits of data without getting overwhelmed. Good interoceptive awareness depends significantly on our ability to feel emotion and solve new problems throughout our lives.

In an article entitled, "Should I Go with My Gut? Investigating the Benefits of Emotion-Focused Decision Making," researchers completed four experiments in attempt to determine the factors that contributed to the best quality of decisions. They state,

> "Results indicate that focusing on feelings versus details led to superior objective and subjective decision quality for complex decisions. However, when using a feeling-focused approach, subsequent deliberation after encoding resulted in reduced choice quality" (Mikels et al., 2011).

Why was Spider Man so successful? He was able to make quick, effective, and accurate assessments of the situation. It's easy to read about in a comic book or watch on television, but living it is a different story. What is that "magic" gut feeling that we experience? I would be a millionaire if I could describe the process of having correct intuition in detail for every situation. My experience as a long-time therapist reminds me that we all develop at our own pace and that frontal lobe and executive function skills vary from person to person.

My sister and I are perfect examples of this. I make decisions quickly and depend on my emotions. I make a list of pros and cons in my head and the process is automatic for me. I rely greatly on my past experiences and life lessons. I never second guess or look back wishing I'd made a different choice. On the contrary, my sister takes a lengthy amount of time to make even the simplest decision. She lists the pros and cons on paper, highlights them, and looks at the list for days. She is rule-governed and a black-and-white, concrete thinker. She considers each option and deliberately builds hypothetical situations in which the choice may work or not work in her life. Who is right and who is wrong? It's subjective and depends on who you, the reader, are and what life experiences you've had. My favorite saying is, "We don't see the world is it is. We see the world as WE are."

SPECIFIC GUIDELINES FOR INTEROCEPTIVE ACTIVITIES

Mindfulness is proven to benefit emotional regulation, sleep quality, and self-esteem; reduce anxiety and depression; increase attention; and decrease anger management issues (Burke, 2009). Clinicians know the neurobiology behind the mindfulness techniques they use during therapeutic work. The best way to improve mindfulness is to work slowly and step-by-step, using fun and engaging activities. As with any technique, client-driven activities are preferred. If you are a parent reading this book, remember that children learn from what they see and from their surroundings. Practicing the activities as a family or together with your child will help to decrease the anxiety, and familial involvement increases outcomes (Kaslow & Racusin, 1994).

Where to begin? It's always best practice to consider a client's cognitive age and functional level instead of their actual age. Many of the children we work with experience delays that do not match their birth age. It's important to begin at a level where you can be successful. Each successful experience builds confidence. Any of the activities can be modified and adapted as you feel appropriate. They are designed to teach awareness of self and to not be too difficult to complete. Remember that children think on a more concrete level. They may require more descriptive instructions and demonstrations.

Games and fun activities involving movement can be more successful as children are generally kinesthetic learners (learn through movement). Kids love making activities into games. Pay close attention to the child's response, and adapt the activity in the following ways:

- Remember KISS (Keep It Simple Silly).
- Use descriptive and child-friendly language.
- Use funny jokes and humor.
- Shorten duration of activities to fit a child's shorter attention span.
- Begin with an activity in which the child is successful. If something's too hard, adapt it for the child.
- Switch roles and ask the child to teach you the skill.
- Complete activities in a quiet setting, free of electronics and other distractions.

Teenagers require unique assistance as they desire to be independent, yet when they are weak in a skill, they need extra support. Depression and anxiety are common if a child has been bullied or feels inadequate. Use extra patience if teens are resistant, and set a behavior contract and clear expectations for students. Review rules of the clinic or session prior to beginning. Remember that hormones are high. The teenage years are critical for forming new neural pathways that can help with mood, emotions, self-esteem, and regulation skills required for complex adult and life skills. Many of my clients are self-conscious, especially in early teenage years. Encourage them to remember that every new skill can be uncomfortable to learn, but the more they practice and "let go" of worry, the better they will become at doing it.

Here are some tips for teenagers:

- Use functional examples such as texting, driving, or studying.
- Focus on health and on building a healthier body for the future.
- Use short- and long-term goals that are realistic and achievable.
- Consider career-building choices.
- Use interests and add to activities to encourage participation.
- Vary exercises and techniques to avoid boredom.
- Focus on relationships and romantic interests.
- Be creative and add arts, crafts, and drama.
- Play teen-friendly music.

Arnold's Interoception Self-Test (Arnold, 2012)

1. Sit in a chair in a quiet location with your hands at your sides and both feet on the ground. Set a timer for one minute, and with your eyes opened or closed (whichever you prefer), attempt to count the number of times your heart beats in that minute. DO NOT hold the pulse on your wrist or neck. Record the number of heartbeats.

2. Next take your pulse for a minute the usual way by placing your left/right pointer and middle fingers on the underside of the opposite wrist. You can also take your pulse by placing your right/left pointer and middle fingers just under the back of your jaw where the jaw meets the neck (on the same side—right or left). Record.

3. Wait two minutes.

4. Take your pulse the usual way again and average the two results attained when taking your pulse, the usual way.

5. Complete the following calculation:

Average heart rate - estimated heart rate
/ average heart rate = Interoceptive Ability

How to interpret your results:

A result of .80 or higher indicates that your interoceptive ability is very good.

A result of .60–.79 reflects a moderately good sense of self.

A result of below .59 indicates poor interoception.

As with anything, these results should be taken lightly, as this is a very informal test of interoceptive skills and may not reflect your sense of self. I'm not entirely sure how accurate this test was at informing me of my own interoceptive skills, but it was interesting.

I find that many of us are visual learners. We learn best when we are shown photos or can create our own mental images. Throughout my years as an occupational therapist, I've created some fun pictorial representations of the inside of our body.

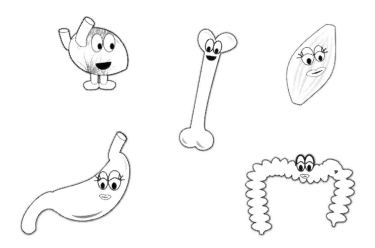

NAMING MY
BODY PARTS

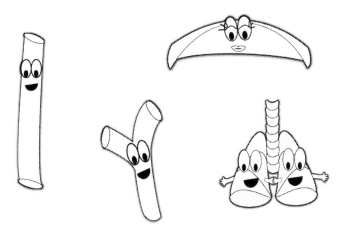

BILLY BONE

My name is Billy Bone. I'm hard and you can feel me under your skin. Feel your elbow. That's a bone! Now feel your knee. That's a bone, too. Your bones hold up your body and help make important cells. Your muscles and tendons attach to bones. Our job is VERY important!

LARRY & LOLA LUNGS

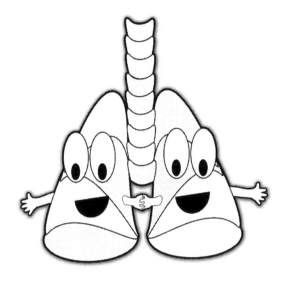

Hi! Our names are Larry & Lola Lungs. We love air and we love you!

Take a deep breath in.

See how your chest expands. That's us!

We get bigger when you breathe in (inhale)—like when you blow up a balloon. We deflate or get smaller when you breathe out (exhale). I hope you know how much we enjoy working to keep oxygen in your body.

MASSIE MUSCLE

Hi, everyone! My name is Massie Muscle. I'm a very important part of your body because you cannot move without me. It's true! Every part of your body that moves uses my strength. Feel your arm just above your elbow. That's the biceps and triceps muscles. Now feel your upper leg. That is the quadriceps muscle and it's very STRONG. Sometimes I feel strong, and other times I feel tired or sore if I'm used too much. I can tell you about what position your body is in. Can you move your arms to the YMCA song? I help you to form each letter with your arms.

BRIGHT BRAIN

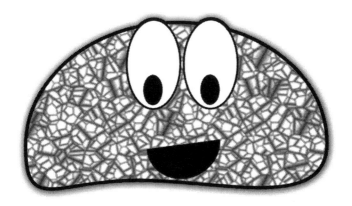

Hello, folks! I'm Bright Brain and I am so important to your body. I am the one who makes decisions or choices. I live inside of your skull (the bone covering your head) so it can protect me. Some people say, "Use your noodle," or "Think about it." They are telling you to use your brain to think about your choices. I sometimes use past experience to help you to decide which action or choice to make. You cannot feel me since I'm inside of your skull and have protective fluid around me. Have you ever concentrated so hard in school or during your homework and felt really tired? That's me telling you it's time to give me a rest break. I can re-charge when you take deep breaths or play outside in nature.

DOLLY DIAPHRAGM

It's so nice to meet you. I'm Dolly Diaphragm, and I help with your breathing. I live in between your chest and your abdomen. In fact, I'm responsible for separating the two areas! I'm the "main muscle of respiration" (breathing). I contract when you breathe in (inhale) and relax when you breathe out (exhale). I love working for you and love when you breathe deeply.

LUB DUB HEART

Pump, pump, pump. I'm Lub Dub Heart. I'm super strong and love moving liquids.

My job is to pump your blood throughout your body. This gives oxygen and nutrients to your different organs, muscles, skin, and body. Did you know you can feel me while I work? Yup. Sit quietly and feel me beating on the left side of your chest. Doctors can hear me with a special tool called a stethoscope. I make the sound, LUB DUB, LUB DUB, LUB DUB. When you are exercising, I pump faster; when you relax or sleep, I pump slowly.

I NEVER get tired and will always beat for you!

ESOPH A. GUS

My name is Esoph A. Gus. I am a hollow tube, but I do so much to help you eat and drink. I'm the tube that connects your mouth and throat to your stomach.

I am made of smooth muscles that squeeze the food to help it move to the stomach for digestion. Sometimes the acid made by the stomach splashes up and makes me feel hot or "burn." It's OK—just let a grown-up know and they can help me to feel better.

SAMMIE STOMACH

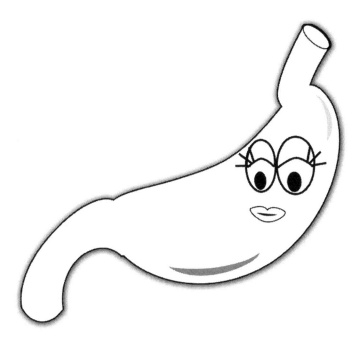

Gurgly gurgle. I'm Sammie Stomach. I love to eat!

I'm made of muscle that contracts and squeezes to mix up and digest the food and drink you put into your mouth. I also release juices that make the food break up into smaller pieces to help it to digest. If you eat too much or get a virus or illness, I can feel awful. When that occurs, I squeeze harder and the food and liquids move up toward Esoph A. Gus and then to your mouth instead of down toward your intestines. This is called vomiting or puking. Sometimes I feel sore when you are worried, scared, or even excited! People often say, "I have butterflies in my stomach!"

SMALLS AND BIGGIE INTESTINES

Hi, friends! We are Smalls and Biggie Intestines. We are sister and brother, and we love hanging out together. In fact, we are a continuous tube. The small intestine connects to the stomach at the top and then connects to the large intestine. This is where the poop or stool is formed from the food you eat. The bottom of the large intestine connects to the rectum, so you can make the poop come out. We are a team, and although we usually work smoothly, we can get sore or feel swollen. Bacteria, a virus, or other condition can make us feel sick and then have diarrhea or have trouble going to the bathroom. Sometimes we feel sore when you are upset, mad, or nervous and make more poop than we usually do. That's a sign telling you that your body may need a rest break or some time taking deep, calming breaths.

VINCE VESSEL

Hello there! My name is Vince Vessel. I'm really neat because I can hold clean OR dirty blood! That's right, I'm flexible. When Lub Dub Heart pumps blood out, I am called an artery and carry blood to your lungs to get fresh oxygen to your muscles, skin, organs, fingers, toes, and even to Bright Brain! Guess what?! Next, I carry back the "used" blood back to Lub Dub Heart and back to the lungs to start the cycle all over again. I never get tired! I'm SO cool that you can see me under your skin. I look like blue web-like tubes. Have you ever taken your pulse on your neck or wrist? If not, I'll teach you how in this book.

Scanning Our Bodies

Now that we have discussed our new friends and their jobs, we can begin to work on scanning our body. Body scans are used in many medical practices, therapeutic clinics, and yoga studios across the world. In fact, since 1994 the National Institute for Trauma and Loss in Children (www.starr.org) has used body scan activity as a part of treatment. Body scans are a newer addition to the practice of occupational therapy as we are learning new information about their benefit in helping us when we experience emotions and in evaluating our overall body status.

Our next job is to identify some common feelings and emotions that impact our lives and bodies: worry, fear, loneliness, impulsivity (wanting something now), happiness, sadness, sleepiness, pain, hunger, thirst, muscle and body fatigue, need for a bowel movement (BM) or urination, fullness (satisfied by food), shallow breathing, butterflies in stomach, hungry hippo in stomach, fire-breathing dragon in tummy, earache, scratchy, pinchy, hot, cold, shivery/shaky, weak, strong, sexual arousal, heart rate, breathing rates, muscle tension, good touch, bad touch, tickling, tension, relaxation, muscle tension, shakiness . . . we link our body signals to our emotions to understand WHAT we are feeling.

Each of us uses different words to describe our feelings. A fun way to develop body awareness is to trace a child's body on a huge piece of paper. Art paper can be purchased at education supply stores. Sometimes we use a large box that is donated from an appliance or home improvement store. Another option is to use a generic body shape as provided in the appendix. Here's one I made:

Label the body with words the child uses to describe her body. Suggestions include basic emotions such as hunger, thirst, pain, etc. Use words the child knows and ask her to label as many as possible. Make it a routine each time she comes into your therapy session, or at a specific time of the day. Ask parents to use the chart when the child mentions a hurt, feeling, emotion, or other physical symptom.

The body scan technique is not meant to be painful or uncomfortable. It's simply a technique to get to know your own body and where certain feelings, pains, or emotions are felt. Since we all have unique past experiences and sensory systems, each of our scans will be different. Many children want to do things the "right way," and it's critical to explain the concept of subjectivity before completing the scan. Review some potential words based on emotions and feelings with the client before the activity so he/she knows what's coming next. I always find it a bit scary to complete this activity on the first session with a child, as closing the eyes requires a level of trust. This is especially the case when working with an individual who has experienced trauma.

Begin by taking some deep breaths, noticing how your own breath feels as it enters and exits the body. Close your eyes if you're comfortable. Remember to begin at the top of the body and ask your client to focus or shine the "spotlight" on each body part. Sometimes, I use an actual flashlight for this activity. Consider the hands, legs, feet, toes, abdomen, chest, skin, brain, eyes, nose, mouth, ears, lungs, and each of the "characters" on the previous pages.

After the body scan and in subsequent sessions, use the labels in the Activity Sheet pack (https://www.pocketot.com/interoceptionbook) or create your own. Review the *naming your body parts clip art* and descriptions while demonstrating on your own body. Cut out the body parts, laminate them, and place them near the anatomically correct areas (e.g., put Sammie Stomach over the location of your stomach). Discuss the feelings of thirst, worry, hunger, etc. with your child. Try using "hungry hippo" and other alliterative terms your child chooses. As with any task, when a child come up with the idea, it's more likely to be followed through as part of the routine.

LEARNING TO LISTEN TO YOUR BODY

When interoceptive awareness is emerging, it can be difficult to understand how to listen to your body's signals. While there's no right or wrong, having a list of questions from which to pull helps us to use words to actively engage the interoceptive sense.

Positional Questions

- Does your body feel comfortable sitting?
- Are your muscles tired and asking you to lay down?
- Does your body feel tired?
- Do you want to rest?
- What type of chair would your body prefer? (note alternative seating options include: bean bags, pillows, a crash pad/mat, t-stool, soft chair, hard chair, seated on a large exercise ball, HowdaHug® seats, wiggle cushion, bumpy chair, or any creative seat you prefer)
- How does your body feel sitting or standing?
- Does your body feel heavy or light?

Sensory Questions

- Are your eyes tired?

- Do your eyes feel scratchy or watery?
- Is your nose clear or stuffed up?
- Is your mouth thirsty or dry?
- Do you hear any sounds that make you feel comfortable?
- Do you hear any sounds that make you feel upset?
- Is your body itchy?
- Do you feel warm or cool?
- Does your body feel like it needs to use the toilet/potty soon? (use words your student understands and are age appropriate here)
- When you swallow how do your throat and mouth feel?
- Do your clothes feel soft (ask about itchy, tight, snug, loose, can you feel seams, etc.)

Organ Friends Questions

- Are any of your organ friends talking to you?
- What are they saying?
- Can you feel Lub Dub Heart beating?
- Is Lub Dub beating quickly or slowly or somewhere in between?
- Is Sammie Stomach making any sound?
- Does Sammy Stomach feel hungry or full?
- Is Sammy Stomach thirsty?
- Does Sammy Stomach feel calm, upset, tight, nervous, have butterflies in him, etc.?
- Is Bright Brain talking to you?
- Does Bright Brain feel sore or tired?
- Is your head tired or sore?
- Did Bright Brain work hard today?

- Is there any burning inside Esoph A. Gus?
- Are Biggie or Smalls saying anything or making noise?
- How is Massie Muscle feeling?
- Is Massie tired or full of energy?
- Do you use Massie Muscles in your legs more when you're standing or sitting?
- Let's exercise Larry and Lola Lungs. Use their names when practicing breathing techniques and incorporate Dolly Diaphragm as you feel her move up and down with inhalation and exhalation.

Activity Suggestions for Body Awareness Scans

- Exercise by jumping up and down and then feeling differences in body parts before and after.
- Drink some water and notice the difference prior to and after drinking.
- Put on a weighted blanket or other item and ask about comfort and if calmness improved.
- Scan before exercise and then after exercise and discuss the differences.
- Put on a coat and discuss differences in body and temperature.
- Eat a snack and notice any differences before and after.

A baby cries to communicate. Most first time parents struggle to figure out what their new baby needs. Crying may signal a dirty diaper, pain, hunger/thirst, fatigue, desire for swaddling, a physiological need for being picked up or rocked (proprioception or vestibular input). The brain's pathways have not yet formed to connect wants and desires. Developmentally, a baby can purposefully smile at the caregiver by three months of age. She is comfortable and associates them with pleasure and comfort.

"You'll do everything in your power to keep those smiles coming. For his part, your baby suddenly will discover that just by moving his lips he can have two-way 'conversations' with you, as his grins bring him even more attention than usual and make him feel good. Smiling also will give him another way besides crying to express his needs and exert some control over what happens to him. The more engaged he is with you and your smiles, and eventually with the rest of this great big world around him, not only will his brain development advance, but the more he'll be distracted from internal sensations (hunger, gas, fatigue) that once strongly influenced much of his behavior. His increasing socialization is further proof that he enjoys and appreciates these new experiences. Expanding his world with these experiences is not only fun for both of you but also important to his overall development" (American Academy of Pediatrics, 2009).

As baby grows and develops, she learns to entertain herself for longer periods of time. Although she will continue to cry as a primary means of communication, the beginnings of social communication emerge. Moving her mouth as if speaking to you, imitating caregivers' movements and facial expressions, and cooing with pleasure when caregivers are near provides reinforcement of the relationship you are quickly developing with your baby. When a baby has a gas bubble as a newborn, she is unable to independently move her body to help it pass. However, as she develops independent movement, she can crawl or move to relieve some discomfort. With each success in learning to comfort and soothe herself, confidence and self-esteem start to build. A certain maturation of the physical, cognitive, and emotional systems occurs as a young child experiences the world around her.

Why is ALL of this important? One of the biggest stressors of a special needs parent is the child's lack of independence in dealing with emotions. Consider a child with difficulty in the area of self-regulation and soothing.

Case Study

James is a fourteen-year-old young man who has been described as gifted. To most, he looks like a typical young teen who is interested in football and video games. However, he is extremely thin and scores in the 10th percentile on the growth chart. His mother describes a common scenario in children who have SPD—he "holds it together" at school and melts down as soon as he arrives home. Additionally, James requires a great deal of assistance with his daily living tasks in both self-care and household chores. He is unable to prepare a simple meal or snack. He also requires assistance with washing thoroughly and needs to be "tucked in" to bed each night.

When he feels upset, he commonly hits both himself and other items around him. James struggles to consider that his current behavior of banging his own feet on the ground yields no results as it's ignored by his parents and sister. Despite his advanced intelligence academically, James shows significant delays in self-regulation, self-care, executive function, sensory processing, and social skills.

As a veteran clinician, I've worked with many families

which include one or more children such as James. The family is commonly stressed, disorganized, and frustrated. None of us is prepared for parenthood; when special needs compound the situation, anxiety and worry increase. Adults forget that the child is experiencing a biological reaction to a stimulus, and it may very well be painful to the child. When there is an over-arousal for long periods of time, such as in school, a child experiences a "crash" or meltdown at the end of the day. We should never say, "Calm down." This is very general and often misunderstood. Instead, the goal should be teaching specific strategies and naming the feelings a child experiences. Making a plan of attack that is on-going and occurs frequently throughout the day builds in chemicals which are designed to calm and slow down the pace.

When we teach our children how to complete body scans and mindfulness exercises, they learn and build new pathways in the brain. Instead of jumping to fight-or-flight reactions, new pathways and connections form in the brain's cortex. We have taught the child a life-long skill of how to self-soothe. As a parent of two children with special needs, and prior to my work in sensory processing and interoception, I did not teach my children self-regulation skills. However, when applying interoceptive awareness and mindfulness skills into our daily routine, our own stress shifts dramatically. We moved from trying to enforce compliance and correct behavior to reducing the causes of the behavior and teaching kids how to help regulate themselves.

Did you know that executive function, housed in the pre-frontal cortex in the frontal lobe of our brain, includes self-regulation? In order to complete higher-level brain processes such as setting future goals and planning, starting, and executing difficult tasks, we need to "decide" what to pay attention to and stop any behavior that's impeding us.

Based on the information you receive/perceive from your body, you identify certain feelings. When my niece is happy to begin school, but at the same time feels nervous, she describes her body as "nerve-cited." Our body gives us information which we call signals, and we interpret them based on our previous experiences, giving individual meaning to them. As the parent of a teenager, I can attest to the fact that he's been "in love" with more than a few girls. However, I know that there is a great difference between being "attracted" to someone versus being in love with someone.

How do we explain this to our children with special needs, particularly those that struggle with idioms and think in black and white, concrete terms? Although this discussion has occurred in many of our homes, the "talk" can be a dreaded part of raising older children. Yes, I'm referring to the sex talk. We order books, look for internet resources, ask wiser adults in our lives, etc. to figure out the best way to go about having the talk. In fact, some families find it so difficult that they never initiate conversation on the topic. Why do we wait until our children are a certain age for the talk? The reasons are basic, but we should discuss them briefly. A young child's brain is simply not ready to handle the complicated nuances of relationships and does not fully understand all the functions of his/her body.

HOW WE INTERPRET AND USE INFORMATION

We often talk about "regulation," but for the purposes of this book and the strategies contained herein, we must be on the same page about its meaning. By design, humans are wired for survival on an individual level and as a species. Safety is sought to preserve ourselves, and sexual desires naturally ensure our survival from generation to generation. Whether you believe in creation or evolution, we all understand there is a circle of life and death. The survival of those without disease and who are healthy means they have a greater chance to pass down their genetic material.

How does our body operate to keep us alive on a daily basis? Buckle up, I'm about to get technical! While I do not usually write in technical terms, it is necessary to understand interoception. Remember from earlier that *homeostasis* is the maintenance of a constant internal environment.

Automatic control systems throughout the body maintain temperature and water at steady levels, which are required for cells to function properly. Strenuous exercise and survival in hot or cold climates affect homeostasis. This includes temperature, blood oxygen levels, hydration and salt levels. Two examples are scuba diving and mountain climbing.

Remember that Walter Cannon's book describes how our body maintains its vital conditions through regulation of multiple systems. Some include: temperature, sodium, calcium, protein, and defense to bacterial/viral invasion. At the same time, our surroundings and even the earth maintain their status among many external and internal dynamics which are constantly changing. Add in our individual motivation and desires as well as the stress which impacts us daily, and things get even more complex. Consider the food chain/web. When events such as El Niño occur, water temperatures rise. Plankton cannot survive, and the organisms that eat the plankton die . . . and so on. Think about the great stories of people in your life and examine real-life heroes in our society. Some lived in poverty, were abused, suffered addictions, or dealt with other horrible conditions, yet they survived and THRIVED! How is this possible? We need to look even deeper at our body's homeostasis to fully grasp interoception.

Our body has receptors inside which signal chemical changes. For example, if our salt levels get too high, our body signals thirst (Fitzsimons, 1979) to dilute the sodium. Pressure receptors in the bladder indicate it is full (micturition reflex) and the process is coordinated by neurons in the spinal cord. When the bladder is stretched, responders let the body know. The "higher brain" determines if there's a restroom near and chooses to wait until it's a convenient time. The process is quite complex, but ultimately, when the person's brain gives signals that his body is sitting on (or standing over) the toilet, the sphincter is relaxed, and urine flows out. It's easy to imagine what might occur if a person cannot determine if his/her bladder is full! (Gonzalez et al., 2016)

When a person travels to a high elevation, many stressors affect his body. The altitude (lower air pressure) makes it more difficult for him to inhale enough oxygen in the lungs. Further, oxygen moves by a process called diffusion from the lungs to the bloodstream. Hemoglobin, a protein, binds to the oxygen and moved through the blood to nourish his muscles and tissue. (Baillie and Simpson, 2017) On a basic cellular level, his body becomes stressed. The question is, "How does he compensate?" The amazing body then produces additional red blood cells and even adds new capillaries to deliver the oxygen more efficiently. The problem is that there are a few who are at a biological disadvantage. According to Goodwin, et. al, individuals with sickle cell anemia were at greater risk of having splenic crises (swelling of the spleen in which blood cannot exit properly) when traveling to higher elevations. This is why some professional sports players with sickle cell anemia do not play their sport in cities such as Denver.

Body Temperature

Think about your experiences. Have you ever been in a room or office with a group of people, and the temperature is set at what is believed to be a neutral temperature? Some in the room feel quite comfortable. Others perceive the room as chilly. A few are sweating or removing sweaters, and their faces redden as they respond to the heat. How could it be that the temperature is the same and everyone in the room experiences it differently? The hypothalamus in the brain detects the temperature in our blood. Since the hypothalamus is the brain's processing center, it is designed to react in a certain way to maintain our own thermostat. Our body is set at 98.6° by design. This is the temperature in which homeostasis is best achieved.

Consider: What happens when you feel hot?

When you feel hot, you begin to sweat. As perspiration evaporates, it cools down our body! It's a literal sprinkler system designed to save you from overheating. This happens when our blood vessels get larger (dilate) to expose the blood to the cooler air around us. Facial flushing is an example. Our blood rushes to the skin and we get red. Touch the redness and it feels hot. So your body has its own "fire department." Awesome! How hot can we get before we experience neurological malfunction and death? The answer: 41.1°C or 106°F.

Heart Rate

In a study published in 2011, Fleming et al. completed a meta-analysis of sixty-nine studies to seek an evidence-based range for heart and respiratory rate. They stated, "Heart rate and respiratory rate are key vital signs used to assess the physiological status of children in many clinical settings. They are used as initial measurements in acutely unwell children, as well as in those undergoing more intensive monitoring in high dependency or intensive care settings. During cardiopulmonary resuscitation, heart rate and respiratory rate are critical values used to determine responses to lifesaving interventions."

In the activity section of this book, I provide instructions for monitoring heart rate. It is true that we can practice activities which are designed to lower our heart rate. How can heart rate be different between humans? Public speaking causes great anxiety for many, but for others who present to groups of people as a part of their work, it becomes routine. The sound of the vacuum cleaner can cause a fear reaction which raises heart rate in some, but the same sound can soothe a newborn baby to sleep. As always, our individual experiences and perceptions drive our physical reactions. Normal heart rate varies from person to person.

Knowing your heart rate is important not only when exercising but also when relaxing. The average heart rate for a child depends on age. Here are recommendations from Cleveland Clinic's website:

Children aged 6—15 years:
70–100 beats per minute at rest

Adults 18 and over:
60–100 beats per minute at rest

The following tables are based on the *Pediatric Advanced Life Support Manual* published by the American Heart Association (2012).

Normal Heart Rate by Age (Beats/Minute)		
Age	**Awake Rate**	**Sleeping Rate**
Neonate (<28 days)	100–205	90–160
Infant (1 month–1 year)	100–190	90–160
Toddler (1–2 years)	98–140	80–120
Preschool (3–5 years)	80–120	65–100
School-age (6–11 years)	75–118	58–90
Adolescent (12–15 years)	60–100	50–90
Adults (15 + years)	60–100	50–90

Normal Respiratory Rate by Age (Breaths/Minute)	
Age	**Normal Respiratory Rate**
Infants (<1 year)	30–53
Toddler (1–2 years)	22–37
Preschool (3–5 years)	20–28
School-age (6–11 years)	18–25
Adolescent (12–15years)	12–20

Blood Pressure by Age		
Age	**Systolic Blood Pressure**	**Diastolic Blood Pressure**
Birth (12 hours)	60–76	31–45
Neonate (96 hours)	67–84	35–53
Infant (1–12 months)	72–104	37–65
Toddler (1–2 years)	86–106	42–63
Preschooler (3–5 years)	89–112	46–72
Young School-age (6–9 years)	97–115	57–76
Older School-Age (10–11 years)	102–120	61–80
Adolescent (12–15 years)	110–131	64–83

Take your heart rate when you wake up in the morning. It's the time when your heart is pumping the least amount of blood since your body is resting and not consuming a great deal of oxygen. Exercise places physical demands on our body to obtain and utilize oxygen, and our heart responds by increasing the rate at which it pumps. Athletes and those in excellent physical condition frequently give their heart a "workout," and as it becomes more efficient, it needs to pump less quickly to deliver necessary oxygen. Stress, medications, temperature, and body position all affect our heart rate. The neat thing is that we can help control and slow our own heart rate with specially designed activities contained in this book.

Stress

Stressful events occur when we least expect them. According to the American Heart Association, "Stress sets off a chain of events. First, you have a stressful situation that's usually upsetting but not harmful. The body reacts to it by releasing a hormone, adrenaline, that temporarily causes your breathing and heart rate to speed up and your blood pressure to rise. These physical reactions prepare you to deal with the situation by confronting it or by running away from it—the "fight or flight" response. When stress is constant (chronic), your body remains in high gear off and on for days or weeks at a time. The link between chronic or extreme stress and heart disease is not clear." We often think of stress as an adult condition. However, it is important to monitor stress in children.

Many of today's children are under great stress. We often see problems in mood, behavior, attention, and physical health. Additionally, motor skills are delayed because of lack of active and outdoor play. For convenience, parents place children in various bouncers, seats, and swings; the use of such apparatuses may decrease baby's ability to move about and explore surroundings. Many children prefer high-action video games and seek out experiences to increase adrenaline. They get used to action-packed adrenaline rushes, and other activities may seem boring. There can be an addiction or "high" associated with this, and children may even attempt to push their limits. Getting back to basics such as taking a walk, riding a bike, playing board games, or chess may help them to learn to slow down their pace. In fact, practicing mindfulness and being relaxed and/or calm is a skill that needs to be TAUGHT and may not come naturally in today's fast-paced and technologically driven world.

Although it is frustrating when function is affected by our past experiences and information stored in our brains, we cannot change our past. This is the case when someone enters the world, or by a traumatic event, experiences physical, cognitive, and sensory difficulties. It's through NO FAULT OF THEIR OWN that this occurs. No one wants to fail. We do the best we can with the equipment (mind and body) that we are given; we often require the understanding and support of those around us to achieve greater success. It truly does take a village!

Signs of Stress

There are many signs of stress. While looking at the following list, consider how stress affects you. When working with someone else, you must know your own responses and attempt to get into your own state of regulation. While this is difficult, it will help you to be in tune with your own body. Also consider the long-term effects of stress. For example, many autoimmune diseases manifest after long periods of stress.

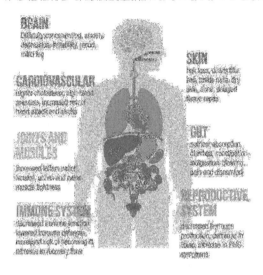

(Younger Chiropractic Clinic, 2017)

Aches and Pains

- Headache
- Pain in neck
- Back pain
- Stomach pain in the form of cramping and/or nausea
- Pain from tightened muscles in specific parts and/or entire body
- Clenched jaw, oral muscles, or TMJ (temporomandibular joint)

Energy Level and Sleep

- Fatigue despite sleep
- Trouble sleeping
- Heightened energy level/hyperactivity with little productivity

Feelings

- Worry
- Anxiety
- Tension
- Fear
- Panic
- Depression
- Helplessness
- Lack of control
- Disassociation (feeling separated from the body and/or experience)

Emotional Signs

- Forgetting/forgetfulness
- Irritation
- Impatience
- Intolerance

How Do You Respond?

When you are under stress, do any of these behaviors apply to you? Jot down other behaviors you notice as you feel stressed. Do the same for your child and work together to keep a written journal to look for trends or patterns over a week or two.

- I engage in illicit drugs, smoking, and/or alcohol.
- I eat.
- I use social media to escape.
- I work.
- I rush around but do not get much done.
- I read.
- I procrastinate.
- I slow down.
- I sleep too much.
- I cannot sleep.

Negative Emotions

Discuss where in/on your body you feel each emotion. Draw arrows on the picture or on the body scan cutout. Discuss possible negative emotions such as: stress, anger, sadness, fatigue, feeling left out, etc. For example, my hands make a fist or clench. Toes curl up in shoes. Face tenses and eyes close a little. Let the person describe in which body part the emotion or feeling occurs. Please remember that every person experiences things differently and processes interoceptive information uniquely. There is NO right or wrong with body scans or any of the activities listed throughout this book.

Make a list of the feelings or emotions that cause physical changes in the body. Examples might include:

- Friends not sharing
- Hunger or thirst
- Fatigue
- Stress of any type
- Hormones
- Social stressors
- Not being able to do something others can do with ease
- Needing to use the toilet or having accidents in bowel and bladder

Positive Emotions

Discuss where on your body you feel the emotion. Draw arrows on the picture or on the body scan cutout. Discuss possible positive emotions such as happiness, joy, fullness, contentment, excitement, enjoyment, satisfaction, etc.

For example, the body may wiggle with excitement. Butterflies of excitement may fly around in the tummy. You may feel a rush of joy and experience a flushed face. Describe in which body part the emotion or feeling occurs. Please remember that every person experiences things differently and processes interoceptive information uniquely, so there is NO right or wrong with body scans or any of the activities listed throughout this book.

Next, list the feelings or emotions that cause the client's body to change or feel differently. Examples might include:

- Trying a new food
- Winning a game
- Making a friend
- Excitement about a good test score/grade
- Using the toilet independently

Using Helpful Words to Show You Care

When helping someone else understand their thoughts, feelings, and emotions we must consider our own views and subjective way of looking at the world around us. I grew up in the era when spanking was perfectly fine. Time outs, the 'silent treatment,' and other forms of punishment worked their way into the mainstream. By the time I had my own children, things were quite different and innovative research showed negative effects or harsh parenting styles. When interviewing members of past generations, phrases such as, "I brought you into this world, I can take you out" and "Stop crying or I'll give you something to cry about" were commonly used.

To best help with interoceptive awareness it's best to establish a partnership with the other person. Giving the person the sense you are working together to figure out how to become more aware helps to provide a comfortable setting. Teamwork and problem-solving instead of demands and punishment help to both establish boundaries and open the relationship for a team approach.

Here are some helpful words to use:

- Let's work as a team as we complete each activity together.
- We can talk about your feelings and worries together.
- When you feel big emotions, let me help you.
- What does your body need to feel comfortable now? We can talk about this later?
- Life is not fair, I agree so let's figure out together how we can tackle this problem.

- Emotions are important and sometimes they get big! I understand and want to help if you'll allow me to.
- It's okay that your body felt upset, let's make a plan for the next time and talk about it together.

Activity: The Jar of Life

Discuss the business of life and how we often feel as though there's not enough time to get everything done in our lives. Talk about or make a list of the activities that NEED to be done versus those that we CHOOSE or prefer to do.

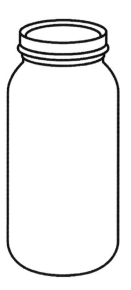

Fill a mason-type jar with river or larger rocks. Is the jar full? Most answer yes.

Next, pick up smaller stones and add them to the jar. Ask the same question: "Is the jar full now?"

Then pour sand into the jar and repeat the question.

Finally, add water to the jar.

Talk about how the jar represents life. The rocks represent those valuable people and things in life: family, friends, and health. The pebbles are important, too. They represent things such as education, house, jobs, car, and clothing. The sand represents the small stuff in life that fills us up, but if we spend too much time on these things, we will not have time for the things that matter. Rocks should be the priorities in life.

Draw circles representing rocks on paper, and name them as the big things that matter most. Next, draw smaller pebbles and list things that are important. Write words around the rocks and pebbles which will represent those "filler" activities such as video games, social media, etc. Remember that this activity will look different for every person. For example, someone with social anxiety disorder may truly NEED social media to realize connections to others. This is a need and not a filler.

Activity: Take Your Pulse

Your heart is literally the rhythm of your body. When its chambers close, the actual sound of "lub dub, lub dub" is audible. Place your right hand over your chest and slightly toward the left side. Feel the beat. When our heart beats, it pumps blood—which is critical for life.

Your pulse is your heart rate, or the number of times your heart beats in one minute. Pulse rates vary from person to person. Your pulse is lower when you are at rest and increases when you exercise (more oxygen-rich blood is needed by the body when you exercise).

How to Take Your Pulse

1. Place the tips of your index, second, and third fingers on the palm side of your other wrist below the base of the thumb. Or, place the tips of your index and second fingers on your lower neck on either side of your windpipe. Demonstrate this for younger children.
2. Press lightly with your fingers until you feel the blood pulsing or tapping beneath your fingers. Sit slowly and move your fingers around a little until you feel the pulse. Use a watch with a second hand, or look at a clock with a second hand.
3. Count the beats you feel for ten seconds. Multiply this number by six to get your heart rate (pulse) per minute.
4. Run in place or do a few jumping jacks.
5. Now repeat to feel the pulse. Notice how it is faster and easier to feel since your heart is now working harder to get oxygen to your muscles and body.
6. Sit and take ten deep breaths slowly.
7. Did the pulse slow down? Is it harder to feel now?

Understanding that our heartbeat can literally change as we increase our activity OR take deep breaths gives us power to know that we have some control over our body! Teach children to take their pulse when they feel different emotions and write it down. Keep track of how the heart rate can increase or decrease depending on taking deep breaths, meditating, closing the eyes for visualization, and completing activities discussed throughout this book.

Activity: Road Blocks

Visualizing can be helpful when considering abstract feelings and emotions. Draw a road map or let the client draw his or her rendition of a road. Ask how it feels when they are overwhelmed or do not have enough time to complete something they wanted to do.

Here are some common answers:

- I didn't have time.
- I forgot.
- I didn't know where to start.
- I was bored.
- It was too hard.
- I didn't have enough help.
- I didn't know how to do it.

We all have obstacles in life. We are often hard on ourselves and have difficulty finding time for things we find tough. Discuss that everyone feels this way and that doing something is better than not doing anything. In fact, doing nothing IS a choice. Draw pictures of the road blocks or add the words to the road and discuss a way to overcome each. For example, when someone does not know where to begin, create a "baby-step" or short-term timeline. If the client reports there was not enough time, set a reminder clock or write the date/time on a calendar.

BREATHING EXERCISES

"Of all the various functions of our autonomic nervous systems, from heartbeat, perspiration, hormonal release, gastrointestinal operation, neurotransmitter secretion, etc., the breath stands alone as the only subsystem the conscious mind can put into 'manual override' and so it is through manipulation of the breath that we can recalibrate the entire system…" (Breathing.com).

Instead of using any of the 'technical' terms for breathing, feel free to substitute our organ friend, Dolly Diaphragm.

One of my favorite therapeutic tools is a balloon! The second favorite is a Hobermann sphere. Teaching breathing is one of the most important skills in interoception. Our entire body is nourished by the oxygen we breathe in. As our life gets busier and we experience stress, our breathing becomes shallower. When we experience a trigger such as a stressful situation, our breath naturally becomes shorter, but many of us do not realize how shallow our breathing has become. This greatly affects the brain's oxygen flow. Light a small candle and show the child how it burns and flickers because of the oxygen. Now, use a mason jar to cover up the candle and watch how the flame quickly burns out due to lack of oxygen. This visual is critical for us to understand how much our own bodies cannot function properly and/or how they "burn out" when we do not receive enough oxygen. If you cannot use a real candle, try a flameless one.

When we inhale (breathe in), we activate our sympathetic nervous system. This causes a stress response. Chemicals released increase our heart rate and cause our blood vessels to constrict; our pupils dilate, and we sweat. We call this our fight-or-flight response, and it occurs when we feel stressed. The part of our brain that is activated is the amygdala. Our alertness increases; tension in our body, including muscles, increases. Our entire body reacts so that we pay attention to the sound. The entire process is designed to protect us from harm.

Breathing out activates our parasympathetic nervous system. It is called our "rest and digest" system. When our bodies are at rest, our heart rate slows down, our digestion is stimulated, and we generally feel more relaxed.

Sensory Breathing

Sometimes children have difficulty realizing the difference between mouth and nose breathing. As an OT, I often teach children how to blow their nose. One of my favorite activates is to make a tissue "dance" by using the nose only. Hold the tissue in front of the child's nose and ask her to cover her mouth. When she blows through her nose, the tissue moves! This is a fun game.

Bumble bee breaths are fun. As children sit comfortably, have them breathe in through the nose and then place the fingers in the ears. Ask them to hum as they exhale. The feeling of the hummmmmmm often feels peaceful and calming. Envision a bumble bee or even use the clip art picture of a bee. (Handouts provided in the appendix.) Now make a buzzzzzzz sound with the mouth while exhaling.

Another idea is to use a light object such as a cotton ball. Encourage a child to blow a small piece of cotton from the edge of the table or off the palm of her hand using her nose only.

Use scented oils, spices, or food to practice smelling in through the nose.

Hyperventilation

Many have heard of hyperventilation, but it's often misunderstood. Despite what many people believe, some experts believe that hyperventilation is caused by too little carbon dioxide, rather than too little oxygen (Esser et al, 2017). The same thing often occurs when people have an asthma attack. Even though hyperventilation makes you feel like you're not getting a deep breath, it is caused by breathing out too much carbon dioxide before you're able to produce more. The pH level in our blood can rise when we suffer from hyperventilation. Also, when you hyperventilate, your blood vessels constrict, and this causes your body to reduce blood flow to the brain.

Symptoms of hyperventilation:

- Chest pain
- Rapid heart rate
- Increased sighing or yawning
- Trouble thinking
- Tingling of hands and feet
- Weakness
- Trouble thinking or "foggy brain"
- Feeling dizzy
- Dry mouth

Mouth

- Blow bubbles
- Blow on a pinwheel
- Blow out a candle
- Blow up a balloon

Belly Breathing

A Hobermann sphere is a plastic ball that is commonly used as a toy but is perfect to illustrate breathing. While you breathe in, expand the sphere or balloon and visualize your tummy expanding. When breathing out, visualize the balloon shrinking and the sphere getting smaller.

Place one hand just above your belly button and the other on your upper chest. As you breathe in through your nose, fill your lungs up with air and feel your belly rise as your chest fills. Make sure to keep your shoulders still! Some of us tend to breathe shallowly and raise our shoulders up and down. While breathing out slowly through your mouth, feel the belly empty and lower. This is a skill that takes practice, especially as we are not used to breathing deeply and shallow breathing has become habitual.

Rectangle Breathing

Draw a rectangle or use your fingers to draw a rectangle in the air while breathing. Breathe in through your nose when you're going vertically, pause when you reach a corner, and breathe out through your mouth when you're going horizontally. The horizontal breaths (exhales) should last twice as long as the vertical breaths (inhales).

One of the best things about using a visual representation of the rectangle is that our children often learn and do better using a visual representation. Once they've practiced many times, children can then visualize the rectangle anytime or anywhere.

Pulse Oximeter

When measuring the amount of oxygen in our blood, medical professionals used to complete a technique called a blood gas test. It involved placing a needle directly into the artery to determine the oxygen levels! Thankfully, pulse oximeters were invented and are readily available for consumers. We bought ours in a local drug store for under $40. The instrument produces a red light as it is clipped on the finger. Within seconds, the heart rate and oxygen saturation level appear digitally on the screen. Remember that some of our clients can become infatuated with numbers, so placing limits on all the instruments and techniques used in the book is critical.

Lazy 8 Breathing

This technique gives children a visual as they use their fingers to trace the eight. They should begin at the star and breathe IN as they slowly move their finger over one side of the eight. As they cross the star at the middle, they should breathe out as they trace the opposite side of the figure. Continue until the child feels calm and relaxed.

Pinwheels

Pinwheels can be found in most dollar stores and come in all shapes and sizes. They naturally work on breathing skills while providing a visual outcome of breathing. Most of us have used them at some point in our lives. Let the student choose the pinwheel style and color. Encourage taking a deep breath in and then blow out emptying the air all the way down to the belly. Try exhaling with the mouth and then the nose!

Elevator Breathing

We have all ridden in an elevator. If a child cannot remember riding in one, take a field trip to a tall building! Draw a picture of an elevator or visualize one. Place the hands one on top of the other, palms down. Keep the left hand as the "ground floor." While breathing in through the nose, slowly raise the right hand as though the elevator is moving upward. During exhale, lower the right hand until it touches the "ground floor" left hand. Repeat, trying to take bigger breaths in to raise the elevator higher and higher. I find elevator breathing to be extremely helpful with children or those who need a visual to learn breathing techniques.

Balloon Breathing

Balloons are one of my top therapy tools. They are perfect for games involving visual perception, gross motor, balance, and so much more. One of the ways to practice breathing techniques is by blowing up a balloon. Use the colors to your advantage. We commonly associate red with anger. Draw an angry face on a red balloon, blow it up, and release it. As it flies around the room, imagine your anger also moving away and deflating, too!

Bubble Use

Bubbles are affordable and easily accessible. Scented bubbles bring an enhanced experience as you blow them and breathe in their calming scent. They are wonderful for the entire classroom or in group therapy sessions. Games where bubbles are caught, popped, and chased provide energy releases and brain breaks for students.

Tummy Breathing with a Friend

Lay on your back and relax. Place your child's stuffed animal, or soft and light object near the belly button for this activity. Think of your breathing and as you breathe in through your nose feel and watch your belly rise. As the child gets more familiar with this task, add bubbles, balloons, and other breathing games mentioned in this book. After counting from three, four, or five (depending on age of child) breathe out and watch the stuffed animal on the belly lower. In my practice, I've found that visuals can be quite helpful to children, especially younger ones or those who have lower cognitive levels.

SUPER ANXIETY BOY...
ABLE TO JUMP TO THE WORST
CONCLUSTION IN A SINGLE SECOND!

CATASTROPHIC THINKING

Mental health professionals know that thinking/assuming the worst possible outcome is common. When we have had many bad sensory experiences, we often feel defeated. One day I bought my son new tennis shoes. He loved them. At the conclusion of the next day of school, he said, "Everybody loved my new shoes!" I felt excited and named some of his friends. "Did Adam say he liked the shoes? How about Julie?" He answered, "No" to each person I named. It turned out that NOT ONE PERSON told him they loved his new shoes; he was showing 'mind reading' behavior.

Ask your child to make a list of thoughts and predictions about different situations in daily life and school. Many times, we 'assume' things are terrible even though there's a solution. This is especially true when someone is having a panic fight, flight, or flee reaction in the moment. It's only when we feel calm again that we have access to higher level thoughts via the cortex of the brain helping with reasoning and solution formation.

How to help:

- Completing regular body scans helps kids to detect signs of stress.
- Write the thought down and talk about it with an adult.
- Ask the question, "Is this happening right now?"

- What can I do about it? Listing actions a child can take during times of worry and rehearsing them often can truly empower children.
- In the past, was this thought true and real, or did the event really occur?
- Children with autism often enjoy math. Use that to your advantage and make predictions based on percentages. For example, make a "How likely is it?" chart.

CATestrophic Thinking Tips

Since use of visuals is so important when teaching a new skill, try my CATestrophic thinking visual. Imagine a cat that's wild and needs to be tamed. The wild cat is messy and needs some food and milk, so he can relax and get comfortable. He's always ready to fight to protect himself. Now imagine a sweet cat living in a cozy warm home with a nice pillow and food whenever he wants it. He's comfortable and is relaxed since he's safe from danger.

Mind-Reading	Everyone hates me. I know my friends think I'm weird.	Billy talked to me today. I am good at history and can name every country in the world.
Guilty Feelings	I should have scored perfectly on that test.	I tried my best.
Labeling	I'm ugly. I'm stupid.	I didn't get the grade I expected, but I know what I did wrong and I will study more next time.
Negative Focus	I missed one question. I spilled the drink on the table, dinner was ruined.	I got 9/10 questions correct. I ate all of my chicken today.
Blaming Others	My teacher didn't explain it correctly. My friend bumped into me.	I can ask more questions if I do not understand. Accidents happen.
Absolutes (always/never)	No one ever talks to me. The whole bus hates me.	Jaden said, "Hi" to me. One person on the bus said, "Ouch" when I stepped on his foot.

Pain Exercises
(Being "OK" With Pain)

Here's an activity idea for older children. Teach them that sometimes things hurt at the moment but they can and will be ok. Place an ice cube in their hand and as it melts, encourage calming thoughts and repetition of the phrase, "I CAN and WILL be ok." The activity is not meant to be painful but to teach that discomfort can sometimes be tolerated for small amounts of time.

Teach the difference between soreness and pain. When we work out or exercise, our body gives us signals to stop or rest. When a person experiences decreased interoceptive awareness, pain receptors may be affected. I once had a client who was bitten by over twenty fire ants and had no idea until his mother saw the bleeding and swollen wounds. He eventually ended up in the emergency department for treatment to stop a life-threatening allergic reaction. On the contrary, some people experience small bumps and touches as extremely uncomfortable. They may have an over-responsive tactile system.

PAIN	SORENESS
Sharp and stabbing, intense	Dull and aching
Requires rest and ice to decrease inflammation	May feel better with movement at a slow pace, may also require ice but stretching helps to resolve discomfort
Lingering	Goes away after 48–72 hours
Occurs immediately, during movement, or within 24 hours of activity	Occurs after 24–48 hours

Adapted from APTA (American Physical Therapy Association)

Self-Control

If you're not familiar with the marshmallow study originally completed by Walter Mischel at Stanford University, I suggest you search for it on YouTube. Several recreations have been made, and some are quite funny. Impulsivity is the opposite of willpower; however, an influencing factor in a person's decisions is having a comfort level or trust in a specific setting. For example, I am going to make a better decision if I'm in the comfort of my own home than in a back alley in the dark.

The pre-frontal cortex of our brain, located just behind our eyes/forehead, is one of the last areas to mature. In fact, the maturation occurs around twenty-five years of age. We use the pre-frontal cortex when we predict outcomes of our choices, consider conflicting thoughts, control impulsive thinking, select what we pay attention to, and even determine how we feel. It's no wonder why children are impulsive . . . they have a lot of maturing to do! I promise it's worth your time to watch the Sesame Street video called *The Waiting Game* here: https://youtu.be/XsC2W587_Fc.

Therapists and teachers know that if a child uses up all his willpower controlling his emotions, he may be too depleted to show a lot of self-control when performing tasks. This is why a child has trouble with decision-making and compromising with others after showing self-control over long periods of concentration. It's been proven that when we are depleted, we are more likely to default to old behaviors, less likely to compromise, more likely to follow impulses, and less likely to trust others. Studies have also proved that self-control leads to higher test scores, happier people, and more successful outcomes in life. So HOW do we help our children with self-control?

As a therapist with years of experience in a rehabilitation unit, I have seen the personality changes when the frontal lobe of the brain is injured. Impulsivity, poor decision making, and uncontrollable cravings may result. In my courses for therapists, I discuss making predictions. It's a strategy that can be fun for kids. It works in the same way as making a hypothesis in science class: "What do you think will happen if . . ."

Additional Activities

1. Encourage children to make predictions about everyday things.

   Examples:

   When watching television, make a prediction about what will happen next or how a certain character might feel.

   During a trip to the park, sit on the bench and observe the other children. Discuss how each child might feel as you watch. Look for a child not sharing his toys; a child pushing someone; kids working together as a team; or a child using kind OR unkind words.

   Ask your child what he/she would do next time to improve the outcome. Draw or write the predictions on paper for those children who need visuals or photos.

2. Ask children to decide between two pre-determined items. When trying to teach a consequence or specific skill, set out the activity and offer two pre-determined options. The child feels more in control since she's making a choice. Discuss how the child might have felt if he/she chose the other option.

3. Cut out pictures from books and magazines. Silly pictures add fun to the activity. Pictures of someone getting caught in a rainstorm, spilling something, carrying smelly trash, tripping, or other action photos are especially fun.

4. Predict what will happen next. Describe a situation or read a story. Stop and ask your child what he/she thinks will happen next. Look on Pinterest for prediction activities. There are some awesome books and worksheets available for free or at low cost. Visit my website at www.PocketOT.com for activity downloads.

Paint Chips as A Therapy Tool

Building supply stores provide paint chips in all colors and textures. Make a list of feelings you have identified or those that represent different body sensations such as pain, hunger, fatigue, etc. Take a field trip (or many) to different home stores' paint departments. Take time to look through the shades and hues of colors. Pull out chips that you or your student feel match certain emotions. Red may indicate evil or the villain in movies but read may cause calm feelings in your body. There is no right or wrong and I encourage you to let the student lead the activity.

Daily life activities can greatly be affected by interoception. Occupational therapists often refer to Dr. Lucy Jane Miller's nosology chart. It is shown here:

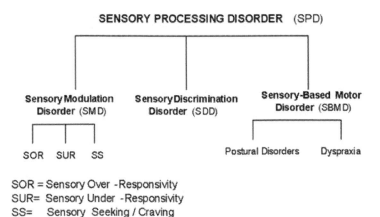

SOR = Sensory Over -Responsivity
SUR= Sensory Under -Responsivity
SS= Sensory Seeking / Craving

Miller Li et al., 2012

When discussing sensory processing, it's important to remember that there are many systems involved. We need to look further into the various types to fully understand how SPD affects our body. Each sub-group may affect any of the sensory areas such as vision, position, interoception, or taste. Therefore, many variations exist and each manifests itself differently in different individuals.

The following are helpful activities to help describe signs and symptoms for each area.

SENSORY PROCESSING DISORDER AND SENSORY ACTIVITIES

Using Your Senses

When we are practicing mindfulness, it's important to use each sense separately. You want to pay attention to each sensation. Focus on it when closing your eyes. Experience each sense as though it is the only thing in the world right now.

SMELL

Did you know that our sense of smell has the only direct connection to the brain? Sensory nerves in the nose provide information directly to the brain's olfactory bulb. That is why when we remember something, there is usually a specific scent or odor associated with the memory. What emotions does the smell of your mother's perfume bring? How about Thanksgiving dinner cooking?

Breathe in and notice any and all smells around you. Bring an item such as a cotton ball with essential oils or pre-determined scents, to your nose. If you're uncomfortable bringing it too close, hold it in your hand and use the other hand to wave air from the object toward your nose. Close your eyes and notice if the smell gets stronger. When you move the item away from your nose, does the smell continue or linger? Does the smell remind you of any past experiences? Do you feel any emotion? How does your body feel when you smell the object?

Some ideas for scents are vanilla, lavender, spices, essential oils, soaps, flowers, outdoor items (grass, pine cones, leaves, seeds, fruits, and vegetables), and foods. Be creative!

When you eat, repeat this exercise because smell and taste are connected. Notice when you have a stuffy nose, your sense of taste and smell are both decreased.

TASTE

When eating, close your eyes and pay attention to the taste. Is it sweet, sour, or salty? Does it make more saliva come into your mouth?

What does the texture feel like on your tongue? Is it smooth, rough, slimy, bumpy, pinchy, prickly, or another word? Can you chew the food using your teeth, or do you swallow the food without chewing it? If you chew the food, is it crunchy? How long did it take you to chew it?

Is the food warm, hot, cool, or cold? Many children need to chew small chips of ice to "wake up" their mouth. Some people use spicy foods or flavors such as "hot" sauce. Others are very sensitive to strong foods like garlic and pepper.

Sometimes, we need to "wake up" our mouths before we eat. Try using a washcloth or towel to massage the outside of the cheeks. Use a vibrating or rotating toothbrush inside of the mouth to prepare muscles for food. Therapy catalogues make fun and colorful therapeutic tools that wiggle and vibrate to stimulate the muscles and sensory nerves in the oral cavity. You can also exercise your mouth and tongue by using a mirror and making funny faces. Ask a friend to make faces and match his face by doing the same thing. Try putting chocolate syrup or whipped crème on the lips and work the tongue and muscles to lick it off.

Activity: Match the Flavor

Combining senses of touch, vision, taste in this activity helps us to understand the everything we eat fits into a category. Ask your child to notice how the saliva in the mouth increases when eating something sour. Make observations when eating together. The game is called 'mindful eating.' Some foods fit into a few different categories below. Everyone experiences taste differently and, in this game, there is no right or wrong.

CHEWY

COLD

CRUNCHY

HOT

MINTY

SALTY

SPICY

SOUR

SWEET

SIGHT

Our eyes work together to give us information about the way things appear. They are designed to differentiate between shapes, colors, brightness, and much more.

Seeing is different from observing. I call this exercise *mindful studying* because when you study something, you truly look at it and analyze it. Pick something up and look at it closely. What shape is it? Does it have a pattern? What are the details that make that item unique? What color is it? Does it blend into the environment or stand out from it? Pretend it's the very first time you are looking at the object. A great example of mindful studying is looking at a tree and noticing all the leaves blowing in the breeze. Each is unique and moves in its own way. The parts of the tree and shades of color truly give it beauty and make it interesting.

Now look at a person. Look at the color of the eyes and other features that make them look both different and then the same as another person. You can try this by looking at yourself in the mirror, too!

Find something that is beautiful to you. Why do you like looking at it? Try to take a photograph in your mind of that object and then remember it when your body feels upset, sad, or stressed.

What is your favorite color? Why do you like that color? Choose paint samples at a home improvement store that match your emotions and look closely at shades and tints.

Use a magnifying glass to look at an item in a new way. Another fun idea is to look up at the clouds to see what shapes they make as they float by.

TOUCH

Our tactile system is intricate and sensitive. As mentioned earlier in this book, our tactile system detects subtle changes in temperature, texture, and details that we use during functional tasks.

Have you ever reached into your purse or backpack without looking to find a specific item? Using your touch sensation to find lipstick, keys, or spare change among many other items in your bag without looking involves *stereognosis.* Each of us has a visual representation of what the item looks and feels like. It may feel smooth, rough, bumpy, soft, cold, cylinder-shaped, plastic, metal, and so on. *Graphesthesia* (writing perception) is when a person closes his eyes and the examiner traces a letter or number in their palm with the fingertip. It's remarkable that someone can identify what's drawn in their palm just by feeling it! Both concepts test higher (cortical) brain levels of somatic sensation. Many other tests are completed by neurologists to determine at what level injury or illness occurs.

Many people with sensory processing difficulties experience great difficulty with light touch. Touch tends to be subjective and varies greatly between individuals. Most of our body is covered with hair. Lijencrantz and Olaussen studied light touch and human skin. There is a definite link to unique touch receptors called C tactile fibers (CT fibers) which are stimulated with light touch. Interestingly, the signal moves through the insula. This is exciting since we know that the insula helps form emotional responses based on our experiences. If a child is raised in an orphanage devoid of touch from caregivers, it's well known that complications ranging from emotional disorders to death may occur. Difficulties in effective sensory processing via our touch/

tactile receptors may greatly affect relationships with others in social situations. Imagine how you would feel if you experienced a fight, flight, or flee reaction when touched by another human. The results might be catastrophic. This is often the case with those who have sensory processing difficulties.

Activity: Mindful seeing

A game commonly found in the therapy clinic is Ned's head. This game uses items that the player can feel within the felt head. Using touch only (not vision) the player must reach into Ned's head to find the object matching a card. You can duplicate this activity by placing items of all shapes and sizes into a shoe box or sock. Examples include: game pieces, beads, keys, blocks of varying shapes and sizes. Place one item into the box or sock and set the other item out in front of the student. Using the hands only to reach into the box, find the matching item.

Activity: Remember 10 items

When I was younger we did not have computers or hand-held devices. Entertainment was provided by making up games. One of the best games was remembering the objects. Place ten (or fewer items for younger kids) onto a tray. Allow the player ten to twenty seconds to look at the items. Take away the tray of objects and ask the player to draw, describe, or write the items they saw on the tray. The activity can be done in the person's room, desk, or at school. Taking note of objects that may cause distraction and confusion encourages organization. Practicing observation skills helps people to take mental notes of their surroundings. The functional carryover of this activity can be quite useful. When a person practices using mindful seeing, he may improve his notice of his environment.

How should we use touch therapeutically?

The concept of therapeutic touch is known across the world. It's a complimentary intervention to traditional medical care. Delores Krieger, PhD, RN, developed the technique in the 1970s. It's based on the idea that our bodies are made up of an energy in the form of a field. According to the Therapeutic Touch International Association (www.therapeutictouch.org), "When you are healthy, that energy is freely flowing and balanced. In contrast, disease is a condition of energy imbalance or disorder. The human energy field extends beyond the level of the skin, and the Therapeutic Touch practitioner attunes him or herself to that energy using the hands as sensors." I've not used this technique but felt it important to mention it as a treatment option.

Weighted blankets involve the tactile system. Feeling the weight and pressure of the blanket on our skin receptors provides a great deal of sensory information to the body. In my book *The Weighted Blanket Guide*, my co-author Eileen Parker and I discuss the various mechanisms and scenarios in which a weighted blanket may be useful. Those with PTSD, fibromyalgia, autism, sensory processing disorder, trauma, and so many others find great benefits with the use of the blankets. Although scientific studies are limited, weighted blankets provide a viable option for those aged three and up (who can individually remove the blankets). As with any therapeutic intervention, ask your doctor or therapist for weight, age, and movement restrictions.

Many classrooms employ weighted, air, and compression vests. Items made by Spio® (www.SpioWorks.com), Under Armour®

(www.UnderArmour.com), and other companies provide squeeze and sensory input to our bodies. I always recommend trying a weighted lap pad first as they are affordable and quite easy to make.

Activity: Make your own weighted lap pad

Simply fill a pouch, pillowcase, or small bag with poly-pellets and place on the user's lap. Many companies sell weighted items with gentle hints of lavender and other calming scents. To make your own, add a few drops of essential oil to the rice or pellets before adding them into the lap pad.

Use knee-high colorful socks to make snake-like lap friends. Place rice or pellets into a plastic baggies and then use duct tape to make sure they stay in a line to fit snugly into the sock. Gently push the line of taped baggies into the sock. Sew the open end or tie it to keep the bags from falling out. I encourage my clients to make a silly face on the weighted sock with markers or gluing google eyes and even a felt tongue! Doesn't it look like a snake? If your child prefers, make a dog or cat sock by cutting out and gluing on felt ears, tongue, nose, whiskers, and eyes. I love it when my clients get creative and personalize their sock buddies.

Massage

Massages provide wonderful relief from stress, pain, muscle tension, and so much more. Adding regular massages to your health and wellness routine can provide tremendous benefits. Massagers created for children and sold in therapy equipment catalogs come in fun shapes. Occupational therapists understand the many benefits of massage in patients with injury, illness, scarring, disability, and more. The hands-on approach provides a holistic benefit to our patients. When stressed, try massaging your feet or tired muscles, noting any improvements in relaxation, lowered heart rate, and blood pressure.

HEARING

I often open and end my sessions with a chime. The pleasant sound lingers for a few seconds and draws the listener into the present. Chimes are available for reasonable prices on Amazon or in yoga stores. Strike the chime and listen to it as it slowly fades. Now, as you sit still and quiet, the background sounds may be more apparent. Listen for fans, buzzing lights, traffic outside, wind, etc. Try not to think about the sound being good or bad; just accept it as it is—a sound. Mindful listening helps when emotions run high or someone feels stressed or upset. Try to name five different sounds heard in the environment to bring focus back to the present and away from the upsetting event.

When I attended the Vital Links® training, I remember learning about sound frequencies and their application to our bodies. For example, high frequency sounds provide detail about the sound. Low frequencies can be alerting. Consider an unexpected clap of thunder. We tend to move into a routine lull or habitual thought patterns, but when thunder booms loudly, we are quickly alerted and pay attention to the outside looking for something dangerous. Our bodies are designed for protection, and danger may be associated with the unexpected noise.

Use music to your advantage. Create a list of songs that soothe and relax you. When you feel stress or emotion rising, turn on one of the songs from your list. On the contrary, make a playlist that wakes you up or makes you feel empowered. I love the idea of choosing a theme song and imagining it's playing when you move to a difficult situation or setting. Therapists understand the power of music and use it to help their clients move toward optimal arousal and regulation levels.

Activity: Phonics Phone or Whisper Phone

Speech and occupational therapists have been using whisper phones for years. They may be purchased from therapy catalogues but the most affordable way to obtain this tool is to easily make your own.

Supplies:

- One straight piece of PVC pipe
- One, 45-degree piece of PVC pipe
- Two, ¾ inch elbow or
  90-degree corner pieces of PVC pipe
- Acrylic paint
- Strong glue or glue gun

Cut the straight pipe into six-inch sections with a handsaw (adults only). Assemble the pieces of PVC pieces into a C shape. Paint in any color you choose.

One of the wonderful benefits of a phonics phone is that when held like a telephone with one side to the mouth and the other to the ear, sounds that sound familiar such as f/v; sh/ch; s/z

Hearing sounds helps kids to learn to match sounds with letters. Whisper phones are awesome to help kids to learn to whisper and/or speak loudly. Controlling the volume of your voice helps with body awareness.

Activity: Dance to the Music

Dancing helps with body position/proprioceptive awareness. Gather different types of music with varying beats. Play the music and dance together to the beat. Dancing in front of a mirror provides a visual bonus for the activity. Move in any way you'd like and then stop the music and freeze in place. Take turns imitating each other's 'frozen' position.

Ask students what type of music makes them feel relaxed, uncomfortable, etc. Try music that the student is not familiar with such as classical, sixties rock and roll, classical, and jazz. Some music such as the CD, *Sacred Earth Drums* by David and Steve Gordon.

- Clap along to the beat
- Use a drum or create your own
  and beat along to the music

Create a rhythm of your own and ask the student to imitate you. Let the student create a beat for another person to imitate. Listening and trying to imitate someone can be fun and adding the game or competition creates another layer of excitement

Activity: Potato Head Senses Game

Use brown felt to make the shape of a potato or use the plastic Mr. Potato Head toy with plastic parts. Each player needs one potato. To prepare, put the different eyes, noses, mouths, hands, feet, ears, and other parts into a bin with sections from the dollar store. Another option is to build a large potato head with clay.

Each player takes a turn spinning the arrow. The sense on which you land is the piece you must put onto your potato. Kids love this game since the potato head might have four noses or three sets of eyes. This game provides a wonderful opportunity to talk about each sense and match some feelings with the body part. Examples include watery eyes when happy or crying; sniffles when feeling sick; fingers tingling when stressed or not breathing properly; etc. The possibilities are endless.

Activity: 5 Senses

Print the shapes onto card stock or laminate it for durability. Poke a hole into the center and use a brad or paper clip for the arrow.

Add words such as ear, eye, nose, hands/feet, and mouth; adapt as appropriate for younger children.

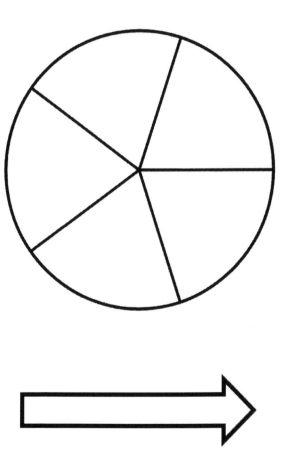

Actitvy: Fact Checking

Events in our lives elicit thoughts or our interpretations of the events. Remember, these thoughts are based on our genetics and past experiences. This activity will help you to look at the facts about the event and help you to process it effectively.

What IS the situation?	
List the facts (what I know) about the situation.	
What are my thoughts or interpretations about the situation?	
Do I feel afraid, scared, or in danger (threatened) by the situation?	
Do my emotions "fit" with the facts?	
What can I do to change my thoughts right now? This can include strategies taught to me such as breathing exercises, fidgets, seeking hugs/deep pressure input, or mindfulness activities.	

Things That Make Me Feel Happy

Outdoor activities
Sleeping
Taking a walk
Organizing
Riding a bicycle
Cleaning
Bouncing a ball
Crafts
Lying in the sun
Listening to music
Going rollerblading
Sports
Going camping
Driving
Singing
Laughing
Exercising
Gardening
Collecting things
Fixing things, repairs
Having quiet time
Painting
Going to a movie
Fishing
Playing a video game
Camping
Yoga
Learning/school
Laughing
Teaching

Vacation
Planning a party/event
Talking with friends
Puzzles, Sudoku
Singing
Money saving/ management
Going to the beach
Sewing
Going to the mall/ shopping
Joining a club
Going on a date
Photography
Religion/beliefs/ praying
Science experiments
Eating
Looking at maps/ directions
Swimming
Selling/trading
Jogging/running
Winter sports
Meeting new people
Being alone
Taking a shower/bath
Being with people
Using a computer
Travel

Playing cards
Playing cards
Taking care of a pet
Babysitting
Writing/journaling
Getting a massage
Cooking
Jumping, hopping, skipping
Learning new things/ skills
Going to the zoo
Working with wood
Dressing up
Politics and government
Looking at fish
Debating/talking about issues
Homework
Chess
Talking on the phone
Board games
Bowling
Blogging
_____
_____
_____
_____
_____
_____

MANY CHILDREN AND ADULTS
HAVE DIFFICULTY STOPPING!

S   Stop, freeze, do not move

T   Take a deep breath

O   Observe your surroundings

P   Plan your response

Emotions, Synonyms, and Physical Symptoms

Every person has specific thoughts and beliefs about what is happening in the environment. When someone has an awareness of something around him, he experiences both psychological and physiological changes. The brain changes as neurons fire, affecting the autonomic nervous system. This changes our heart rate, temperature, breathing patterns, muscle tone, and many other things. We then use various facial expressions, words, actions, and behaviors to show how we feel on the inside. Remember that everyone interprets experiences differently and thus reacts in different ways. Use the "Common Word" chart (p. 132) to help someone describe how they are feeling during an emotional reaction. This can help them choose a strategy to help their body move toward a more calm and regulated state. Remember to draw an animal or visual representation of the emotion as often as possible to increase awareness and connections to the body. For example, anxiety alligator is chomping mad or a sad puppy whines and pouts. Use the body chart and our animated organs to show where the feelings "live" or exist in the body.

It's important to consider all the words used to describe emotions. I encourage you to reference a thesaurus with your student to make lists of alternative words. For example, I searched sadness in several places and found these synonyms: alone, agony, woe, disappointment, suffering, gloom, lonely, depression, neglect, disappointment, hurt, pity, unhappiness, gloomy, rejection, disconnected, despair, defeat, insecurity, crushed, tears in eyes, butterflies in the stomach, shaky body, pit in the tummy, aches and pains of body, not hungry, fearful, headaches.

Common Word: Sadness	Common Word: Love	Common Word: Happiness	Common Word: Fear	Common Word: Anger
Hurt	Adore	Joy	Scared	Agitated
Depressed	Caring	Hope	Worry	Furious
Lonely	Passion	Pride	Frighten	Rage
Misery	Kindness	Excited	Angry	Grumpy
Jealous	Compassion	Cheerful	Nervous	Frustrated
Gloomy	Fond	Content	Dread	Flustered
Bummed	Crush	Sunny	Panic	Upset

Make a chart out of poster board or on a large chalkboard or whiteboard. I often choose a "feeling of the week" and let my students list their emotions or where in their body the specific emotion is felt. This can be fun as we often experience similar feelings but, due to communication differences, cannot use descriptive language. Adults can use this during staff trainings and mindfulness activities.

Sensory and Calm Rooms

Occupational therapists understand the benefits of cool down, sensory, Snoezelen, and calm rooms. While they are named differently, their purpose is the same: to help students regulate the sensory system in times of crisis and escalation. Trauma-informed care is bringing awareness to the mainstream about calm rooms, and an OT is a perfect team member to add when considering design.

The goal of any sensory room is to create a safe space for a child who is showing signs of behavioral and emotional meltdown. As always, the goal is to be proactive and learn to identify the physiological signs of a meltdown well before it occurs. Remember that a child should be supervised in the room because in a state of fight or flight, chemicals drive the reaction and injury is a real possibility. The goal is to nurture and support the person using the calm room and NOT to punish the person using it.

One of the biggest questions I receive is, "What should we include in a sensory or calm room?" Let's begin with the floor. Gym mats or soft foam tiles provide cushion and dampen sound if the child is pounding or thrashing. Pillows, crash mats, bean bags, fabric "rocks" filled with cushiony material, and soft seating provide wonderful input to the body. Walls should be uncluttered, and the lighting is best when it's soft and/or a color that is calming. Paint colors such as red and orange are generally avoided. Amazon and special-needs equipment catalogs sell fire-resistant fabric and covers for fluorescent lighting. I'm noticing more dentist's offices using similar coverings to calm their patients.

Here is a list of other items frequently used in sensory rooms:

- Music with headphones
- Noise-canceling headphones to dampen loud sounds such as fire alarms and noisy hallways
- Breathing cards and instructions on how to take deep breaths to provide oxygen to refresh the brain after a meltdown
- Sand, rice, and other bins filled with safe materials for tactile stimulation
- Books and social stories with "how to calm" instructions
- Oral motor toys such as Chewigems®, gum, or liquid to drink through a coffee stirrer to provide heavy work for the mouth muscles
- Lotion containing scents such as lavender and vanilla
- Rocking chairs and suspension equipment (These must be supervised, but when used properly, they can truly calm the vestibular system. It's important to consult an occupational therapist prior to use of any suspension equipment. Movement back and forth and side to side can be calming, while swinging in a rotary or unpredictable pattern may provide too much alerting stimulation.)
- Drawing, coloring, or water paints to provide a creative outlet
- Bubble tubes, light projectors, fiber optics, color switches, and wall panels (These cost more but create a truly wonderful sensory environment. Many people choose holiday lighting, but some cords contain lead-based paint and are not fire safe.)

TOILETING AND INTEROCEPTION

One of the most frustrating and biggest areas of difficulty affecting our children is toilet training. For some, the task is seamless and very few accidents occur. However, a common thread in children who lack interoceptive awareness is difficulty with toilet skills.

The urge to urinate or have a bowel movement can feel intense for some and be almost undetectable for others. Many children with whom I work simply do not feel the pressure and input from the bowels and rectum. They seem to have constipation frequently. Sometimes a humiliating bowel or bladder accident in a public location causes a child to have a great deal of anxiety regarding using the toilet. On the other hand, children who perceive sensory information too intensely might describe the feeling of a full bladder or rectum as extremely painful. There is no correct answer as we are all wired differently. However, we can help our children to understand their bodies better with the addition of helpful wording and a toileting chart.

A question I'm asked frequently is, "Why does my child pee in the toilet but ask for a pull-up to poop into?"

The feeling of stool or urine leaving the body many be uncomfortable for some of our children or they may feel 'empty' or out of control when the wastes leave the body. Another explanation is that having a bowel movement requires pushing.

The feeling of pushing poop into the toilet gives no 'feedback' or touch/tactile sensory information to the outside skin near the rectum. Pushing poop out and feeling it move to the pull-up gives some tactile feedback.

Further, attention of a child may contribute to the desire to have a bowel movement in a pull-up. To sit on the toilet requires a child to stop what he's doing and take time to sit. Some options include:

- sitting with your child as he is on the toilet
- giving him a special toy to play with while on the toilet only
- drawing on the back of the toilet with dry-erase markers
- creating a spa-like atmosphere to help comfort and relax your child
- add a special potty toy or relaxation box with cremes containing calming scents, a sticker reward chart, sensory fidgets
- place food coloring in the toilet water. Blue can change to green as your child adds his yellow urine
- purchase a special potty for your child and let him decorate it with stickers or markers
- use calming music in the bathroom
- read books about potty training
- Call attention to your child's body and feelings as he uses the potty. Ask, does your belly and biggie and smalls intestines feel better after you pooped? Can you feel the pee leaving your body? Use the body scan tool or the body characters found in the "Naming My Body Parts" section (p. 51) of this book.

Other Considerations:

- Rule out medical reasons why a child may be experiencing toileting problems.
- Consider that the child may experience a lack of independence in dressing skills (such as zipping, buttoning, or fastening snaps) that can contribute.
- Receptive and expressive language delays might create communication barriers for our children.
- Sensitivity to loud flushing toilets, feeling of the cold seat, the high-blast hand dryers, and other sensory concerns may contribute.
- Transitions are frequently difficult for children. If a child is busy playing, she may not be able to swiftly transition to the toilet when she feels the urge.
- Routine helps to build structure for our children. Using toilets in various public locations can be a source of great anxiety.
- Smells released during bowel movements sometimes cause sensory overload.

In your child's planner or on a calendar page, write the times of day your child eats. Now, insert times designated for using the toilet. As the gastro-intestinal tract begins digesting, it also moves rhythmically, thus causing the need to use the toilet. I suggest planning to use the toilet half an hour after eating a meal. Now, add a potty break first thing in the morning and just prior to bedtime.

Remember that using visual schedules helps many children to incorporate critical steps into their daily routine.

Teaching Wiping Skills

Hygiene is critical to people of all ages and understanding how to clean after a bowel movement is critical to prevent infection. As a clinician working with children and adults, I have learned a few strategies to pass on. Many pharmacies and medical equipment stores have long-handled mirrors. They are often used by patients after amputations to check the remaining portion of the leg and/or arm for redness and sores. A self-standing mirror that tilts can be invaluable when learning wiping.

Sitting backward on the toilet can give stability to those who need to hold onto something. The back of the toilet can be quite supportive when posture/core is weak. Use wet wipes or cleansing cloths. I recommend cutting them in half for smaller children.

Remember that females need to wipe from front to back to avoid infection. Practice cleaning sticky substances from fruit such as a peach or apricot. As gross as it sounds, it really can help people to understand the pressure requirements on the bum. Use peanut butter, chocolate, or whipped cream.

Blow up a balloon halfway and make a crack in the middle with your fingers or with duct tape. This is designed to represent the bum. Add peanut butter or other sticky substance to the balloon in the cracked/grooved area. Use real toilet paper to practice.

Sensory Diet to Regulate Toileting and Interoception

Sensory activity diets are frequently recommended for overall sensory regulation. The goal is to add a sensory activity every few hours to provide consistent input to the body. People of all ages can and should complete breaks every two hours as they work or are seated for long periods of time. Including any "heavy work" means pushing, pulling, lifting, or carrying with the large or gross muscles of the body. Heavy work does not mean purchasing weights and implementing a strict exercise routine, it means doing activities that work the large muscle groups of the body. Here's an example: while standing at least a foot away from the wall, place your hands on the wall at mid-chest height. Now, lean your body into your arms like doing a push-up on the ground. Students often carry a stack of books to the library or office, use weighted lap pads, or complete wall or chair push-ups. Other activities commonly include swinging, trampoline jumping, chewing on crunchy food, using body socks, using fidget items for the smaller muscles of the hands, and using resistive exercise bands.

Therapeutic brushing is a great strategy to provide input to the body. This week a parent's physician recommended brushing for her daughter. He simply told her to use a brush to move slowly and with medium pressure over her arms, legs, and trunk. Mom used a regular stiff-bristle hairbrush for the technique. As soon as she showed a picture of the brush and her technique, I was filled with concern. The brushing program is officially called

The Wilbarger Deep Pressure and Proprioceptive Technique, or DPPT. The name comes from both the brushing and joint compressions that provide input to the body. It involves much more than simply using a brush on someone. There are timing and activity considerations as well. Patricia Wilbarger is an occupational therapist who initially developed the technique of therapeutic brushing and the sensory diet. Did you know that there is an oral (mouth) swipe that's a part of the program? I strongly suggest readers go to www.campavanti.com and www.childdevelopmentmedia.com for more information about Patricia and her daughter, Julia, as well as the specific soft surgical brushes used for her program (Wilbarger and Wilbarger 2002).

> ****UNDER NO CIRCUMSTANCES** *should any person complete any brushing and/or deep pressure program until formal training is obtained since results may be either ineffective or harmful.*

WHAT IS MINDFULNESS?

The concept of being mindful is not new. The goal is to become aware of the present moment. How many times have you driven to work and then thought, "I don't even remember driving here"? We tend to live in the rote (routine) doldrums of everyday life. Routines and automaticity get us through our busy day. Additionally, we fear judgment and/or not being accepted by our peers, and we often think about our past. Many dream about the past and how it would have been if different choices were made. Many times, we idealize the past as a coping mechanism to deal with issues. Psychology Today discusses how we, "reconstruct memories to adjust to our current situation—and sometimes these revised memories even help us in ways we don't realize" (https://www.psychologytoday.com/blog/the-young-and-the-restless/201112/the-process-idealization).

Being mindful permits us to live in the current moment, appreciating the smells, sights, and sounds of the present. Mindful individuals let go of evaluating themselves and grab on to the current moment. There is no "right" place to be. In fact, this concept can be practiced anywhere, anytime. It means quietly focusing on body sensations, thoughts, and emotions as we feel them. Listening to and feeling our breath and connection to those around us is mindful. Keeping our minds open to new experiences and stopping judgement and harsh criticism of ourselves is mindful. Although mindfulness can be associated with yoga and spiritual practices, mindfulness can occur anywhere and is not unique to any religion.

There are two important states of mind to which I refer in my practice: hot minds and cool minds.

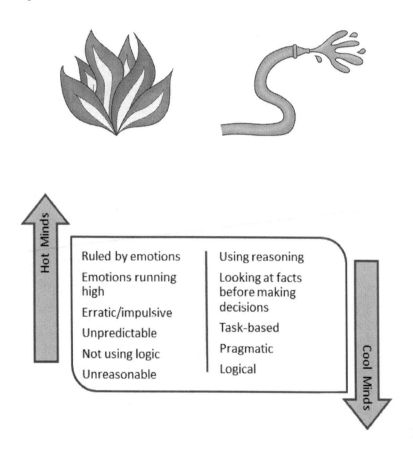

Hot Minds

Ruled by emotions

Emotions running high

Erratic/impulsive

Unpredictable

Not using logic

Unreasonable

Using reasoning

Looking at facts before making decisions

Task-based

Pragmatic

Logical

Cool Minds

Activity: Hot and Cold

Print out and laminate the fire to represent **Hot Minds** and the hose/water to represent Cool Minds. Use any type of media such as magazines, photos, feelings cards, etc. to show examples of times, faces, and/or emotions that you feel belong in each category. Place those that don't fit either category into a third category. This category can be called the **Middle Ground**. The middle ground represents times when there is no solution, but compromise is the answer.

Place the smaller **Hot Minds** and **Cool Minds** graphics on the part of the body where you feel the emotion. For example, angry people often describe their face as being hot. Other common areas where people can feel heat or anger are in the stomach, feet, hands (sometimes when aggressive), or head/brain.

Activity: Butterflies in My Stomach

Many times, we feel emotions in our organs. A common report is "nervous tummy" or "butterflies in my stomach." Print out butterflies or cut them out of magazines or old books. Talk about emotions that cause excitement, worry, fear, sadness, and many others that cause physical sensations in the stomach. Glue the butterflies onto a piece of paper or use a paper clip or clothes pin to place them on a line or fishing wire stretched over the table to create the illusion that the butterflies are flying. Releasing the butterflies can be a powerful therapeutic tool for people of all ages.

Talk about strategies including activities, eating, drinking water or juice, people, songs, memories, sensory strategies, or whatever helps the client to feel "better" or takes the butterflies away. I find it helpful to write the feelings and emotions on the back of the butterflies and visualize or pretend the uncomfortable things are flying away with the butterfly.

Some clients prefer to keep the butterflies in a box and re-use them as a tool for managing difficult emotions and feelings.

Activity: Body Awareness

How does your body feel when it's relaxed? Mine feels heavy, warm, and comfortable. To illustrate this abstract concept, we need to practice relaxation. Lay down on the back (supine) on a soft mat or surface. Ask the student to close his eyes and take deep breaths. In a manner similar to a Savasana (corpse pose) in yoga class, speak softly and slowly as you provide cues to relax. Here's an example: feel your body as it lets the floor support its weight. Squeeze your toes tightly and then relax them. Move up to your legs and progress in the same way (continuing to name specific body parts) until you get to the face. Encourage the student to tense the facial muscles and relax them too.

- Feet and toes
- Knees
- Upper legs
- Belly
- Back

- Hands and fingers
- Lower arms
- Upper arms

- Shoulders
- Neck
- Face

Talk about how their body may feel heavy or calm. Let the student describe his own body's feelings and current state to you as he may use words such as 'floating,' 'cool,' or other subjective terms.

STORIES

Occupational therapist Emmy Vadnais

I worked with a fifteen-year-old who had trouble falling asleep at night. I taught her a progressive body relaxation with physically tensing and releasing muscle groups to the count of five, holding for a moment to feel the tension, and then slowly letting it go to the count of five. She says she uses it every night and can fall asleep more easily. It used to take her 20–60 minutes to fall asleep. She says it now takes her 10 minutes. This is truly a progressive body relaxation. It's important to remember "classic" relaxation techniques, too.

The same client was experiencing stress and avoidance with a sibling who had their own emotional and stress challenges. I guided her in an interactive mindfulness meditation with abdominal breathing, guiding her to connect with her kind, compassionate, loving, and non-judgmental self. I had her notice what feelings, thoughts, and emotions came up connected to her sibling. She described feeling frustrated and feeling tension in her abdomen. I had her observe the frustration and body sensation feelings with her kind self, while simultaneously feeling them, and after ten minutes it subsided. She was able to tolerate her sibling a little bit better and with more compassion.

Jane, parent of Billy

My son has always been a fantastic eater. He eats a wide variety of foods and healthy portions. He prefers to eat carbs but will eat vegetables, fruit, and meat as well. Shortly after he turned five, he started complaining about meat and some vegetables being "too chewy" and hurting his teeth. We took him to the dentist, who said nothing was wrong with his teeth. This continued for eight to nine months, and it seemed to be getting worse; there were nights when he would cry because it hurt so much. After another trip to the dentist, I decided to see if we could find something for him to chew on that would help. I bought chewy necklaces, but he wasn't interested in using them after a few days. Then I decided to see if chewing gum would help. We bought the "healthiest" gum we could find and started letting him chew gum for fifteen to twenty minutes before dinner. After few weeks, he started eating meat and vegetables again and was no longer complaining about his teeth hurting. It's been six months since we started giving him gum, and he hasn't complained about his teeth hurting or about the food being "too chewy" since then. We now let him chew on gum when we notice him chewing on his clothes and, at times, he can identify when he needs to chew the gum on his own.

Special education teacher
Cyndi Blount O'Toole

My son is sensitive to sounds but will not wear his noise-canceling headphones at school. He has exceptional behavior at school and is excelling in all areas. His teachers at school are shocked when we share stories of his behavior at home. One day, after a particularly hard night at home and a hard day at school because the cafeteria was too loud, I was talking to my son about how well he does at school and how hard it is for all of us at home. He said, "I keep all of my feelings in at school, and when I get home, I let them out because I know I can." This made me cry because this is a five-year-old who has learned that his feelings are not socially acceptable at school, but that home is a safe place for him to be him. This comment changed my perspective of his behaviors at home, and I think it has helped both my husband and I deal with challenging behaviors with a little more understanding and compassion.

Mary, parent of Jane

My daughter was in counseling treatment for OCD earlier this year. Part of her treatment included planned exposures to the things she was avoiding due to her OCD thoughts—meaning she had to touch and hold the things she was afraid of due to her fear of germ contamination. The counselor used interoception either during or after exposures or both, as he asked her to describe how her body was feeling (heart rate, stomach, breathing, etc.). I asked my daughter if that helped her and how, and she said it was a useful way for her to understand and recognize how her body was reacting to the thoughts she was experiencing. She said overall it did help her to better tune in to and gauge her anxiety level.

I myself began exploring mindfulness during these experiences with her. I realized that when I was feeling anxious, my breathing was shallow. I never really understood the power of diaphragmatic breaths until I tied it to the stilling of the mind that you do (or at least strive to do) when being mindfully present. Now I can quickly recognize my shallow breathing due to anxiety when it comes; then I can take some mindful moments combined with breathing to dial down that anxiety and re-focus.

My teen daughter will continue to consider using and learning about mindfulness—likely through a yoga place near us that incorporates mindfulness—to help manage her anxiety. She is open to it, but just like all of us, needs reminders to utilize these strategies and tools! She has not taken any medications, as we would prefer to see if her young, malleable brain can instead use education, self-awareness, self-compassion, and strategies for anxiety and OCD management instead. I honestly think OTs could be a great adjunct service to OCD exposure therapy treatment IF the OT is an expert in the condition, how it works, and the evidence-based treatment approaches.

RESOURCES

Ackermann, H. & Riecker, A. (2004). The contribution of the insula to motor aspects of speech production: A review and a hypothesis. *Brain Language*, 89, 320–328.

American Academy of Pediatrics (2009). Caring for Your Baby and Young Child: Birth to Age 5 https://www.healthychildren.org/English/ages-stages/baby/Pages/Emotional-and-Social- Development-Birth-to-3-Months.aspx accessed 12/5/17.

Anderson, T. J., Jenkins, I. H., Brooks, D. J., Hawken, M. B., Frackowiak, R. S., & Kennard, C. (1994). Cortical control of saccades and fixation in man. A PET Study. *Brain*, 117, 1073–1084.

Arnold, C (May/June 2012) Inside the Wrong Body. *Scientific American Mind*, 23, 36–41 Published online: 16 April 2012 | doi: 10.1038/scientificamericanmind0512–36.

Baillie, K., and Simpson, A. (2018). High Altitude. Altitude.org. Accessed 1/23/2018.

Baliki, M. N., Geha, P. Y., & Apkarian, A. V. (2009). Parsing pain perception between nociceptive representation and magnitude estimation. *Journal of Neurophysiology*, 101, 875–887.

Barlow, D. H., Craske, M. G. (2007). *Mastery of your anxiety and panic* (Fourth edition). Oxford: Oxford University Press.

Borovsky, A., Saygin, A. P., Bates, E., Dronkers, N. (2007). Lesion correlates of conversational speech production deficits. *Neuropsychologia*, 45, 2525–2233.

Brown, S., Martinez, M. J., & Parsons, L. M. (2004). Passive music listening spontaneously engages limbic and paralimbic systems. *Neuroreport*, 15, 2033–2037.

Butti, C. Brain Struct Funct. 2010 Jun; 214(5–6):477–93. doi: 10.1007/s00429-010-0264-y. Epub 2010 May 29.

Clark, L., Bechara, A., Damasio, H., Aitken, M. R. F., Sahakian, B. J., & Robbins, T. W. (2008). Differential effects of insular and ventromedial prefrontal cortex lesions on risky decision-making. *Brain*, 131, 1311–1322.

Craig, A. D. (2009). How do you feel—now? The anterior insula and human awareness. Nature Reviews: *Neuroscience*, 10, 59–70.

Craig, A. D., Chen, K., Bandy, D., Reiman, E. M., (2000). Thermosensory activation of insular cortex. *Nature Neuroscience*, 3, 184–190.

Critchley, H. D., Mathias C. J., & Dolan, R. J. (2001). Neural activity in the human brain relating to uncertainty and arousal during anticipation. *Neuron*, 29, 537–545.

Critchley, H. D., Wiens, S., Rotshtein, P., Ohman, A., Dolan, R. J. (2004). Neural systems supporting interoceptive awareness. *Nature Neuroscience*, 7, 189–95.

Damasio, Antonio. (2012). Self Comes To Mind: Constructing The Conscious Brain. Vintage Books.

Dronkers N. F. (1996). A new brain region for coordinating speech articulation. *Nature*, 384, 159–161.

Dunn BD, Galton HC, Morgan R, Evans D, Oliver C, et al. (2011) Listening to your heart. How interoception shapes emotion experience and intuitive decision making. Psychol Sci 21: 1835–1844. doi: 10.1177/0956797610389191

Encyclopedia Britannica, Inc., 2016. Sir Charles Scott Sherrington. Web. 07 Nov. 2016. <https://www.britannica.com/biography/Charles-Scott-Sherrington>.

Ernst, M., & Paulus, M. P., (2005). Neurobiology of decision making: a selective review from a neurocognitive and clinical perspective. *Biological Psychiatry*, 58, 597–604.

Ernst, M., Bolla, K., Mouratidis, M., Contoreggi, C., Matochik, J.A., Kurian, V.S., et al., (2002). Decision-making in a risk-taking task: a PET study. *Neuropsychopharmacology* 26, 682–691.

Barb Norman, Daubenmier Jennifer, Price Cynthia J., Gard Tim, Kerr Catherine, Dunn Barnaby D., Klein Anne Carolyn, Paulus Martin P., Mehling Wolf E.

Esser, Y., Hansman, H., van Dixhoorn, J. (2017). Anxiety, hyperventilation complaints, and dysfunctional breathing. Biological Psychology, Volume 129, 380, 31 October 2017.

Farb, N., Daubenmier, J., Price, C. J., Gard, T., Kerr, C., Dunn, B. D., Klein, A. C., Paulus, M. P., Mehling, W. E., (2015). Interoception, contemplative practice, and health. Frontiers in Psychology. Front. 09 June 2015 | https://doi.org/10.3389/fpsyg.2015.00763

Fitsimons, J. T. The Physiology of Thirst and Sodium Appetitie. (1979). Cambridge University Press.

Fleming, S., Thompson, M., Stevens, R., Heneghan, C., Plüddemann, A., Maconochie, I., Mant, D. (2011). Normal ranges of heart rate and respiratory rate in children from birth to 18 years: a systematic review of observational studies. Lancet, 377(9770), 1011–1018. http://doi.org/10.1016/S0140-6736 (10)62226-X

Garfinkel, S.N., Seth, A.K., Barrett, A.B., Suzuki, K., Critchley, H.D. (2015) Knowing your own heart: distinguishing interoceptive accuracy from interoceptive awareness. *Biological Psychology*. 2015 Jan; 104:65–74. doi: 10.1016/j.biopsycho.2014.11.004. Epub 2014 Nov 20.

Godwin, M. J., Embury, S. H., & Claster, S. (1981). Risk of Altitude Exposure in Sickle Cell Disease. *Western Journal of Medicine, 135*(5), 364–367.

"Heatstroke" – Robert S. Helman M.D., eMedicine (2016).

Heller, L., LaPierre, A. (2012) Healing Developmental Trauma: How Early Trauma Affects Self-Regulation, Self-Image, and the Capacity for Relationship. North Atlantic Books Volume 11 of the series Current Topics in Neurotoxicity pp 313–334 Date: 09 October 2016.

Hunter, S., and Donders, J (2007). Pediatric Neuropsychological Intervention. Cambridge University Press, Cambridge, UK. **Chapter cited by Tara Spevaek.

Hsu, M., Anen, C., & Quartz, S. R. (2008). The right and the good: Distributive justice and neural encoding of equity and efficiency. *Science*, 320, 1092–1095.

Karnath, H. O., Baier, B. & Nagele, T. (2005). Awareness of the functioning of one's own limbs mediated by the insular cortex? *Journal of Neuroscience*, 25, 7134–7138.

Kirk U, Downar J, Montague PR (2011) Interoception drives increased rational decision-making in meditators playing the ultimatum game. Front Neurosci 5: 49. doi: 10.3389/fnins.2011.00049.

Kolb, B., & Whishaw, I. Q. (1998). Brain plasticity and behavior. *Annual review of psychology*, *49*(1), 43–64.

Koscinski, C.N., (2016). Parent's Guide to Occupational Therapy for Autism & Other Special Needs. Jessica Kingsley Publishers, Philadelphia, PA.

Koscinski, C. N., & Parker, E., (2016). The Weighted Blanket Guide book. Jessica Kingsley Publishers, Philadelphia, PA.

Kuhnen, C. M., & Knutzon, B, (2005). The neural basis of financial risk taking. *Neuron*, 47, 763–770.

Ladabaum, U., Minoshima, S., Hasler, W. L., Cross, D., Chey, W. D., Owyang, C. (2001). Gastric distention correlates with activation of multiple cortical and subcortical regions. *Gastroenterology*, 120, 369–376.

Lazar SW, Kerr CE, Wasserman RH, Gray JR, Greve DN, et al. (2005) Meditation experience is associated with increased cortical thickness. Neuroreport 16: 1893–1897. doi: 10.1097/01.wnr.0000186598.66243.19.

Lee, K., Noda, Y., Nakano, Y., Ogawa, S., Kinoshita, Y., Funayama, T., & Furukawa, T. A. (2006). Interoceptive hypersensitivity and interoceptive exposure in patients with panic disorder: specificity and effectiveness. *BMC Psychiatry*, 6(1), 32.

Lewis J. G. (2015) Smells Ring Bells: How Smell Triggers Memories and Emotions. *Psychology Today*. https://www.psychologytoday.com/blog/brain-babble/201501/smells-ring-bells-how-smell-triggers-memories-and-emotions.

Liljencrantz, J., & Olausson, H. (2014). Tactile C fibers and their contributions to pleasant sensations and to tactile allodynia. *Frontiers in Behavioral Neuroscience*, 8, 37. http://doi.org/10.3389/fnbeh.2014.00037

Marneros, A.M. (2008). Psychiatry's 200th birthday. *The British Journal of Psychiatry*, 193:1–3.

Miller, L.G., Anzalone, M. E., Lane, S.J., Cermak, S.A., Osten, E.T., Concept Evolution in Sensory Integration: A Proposed Nosology for Diagnosis. American Journal of Occupational Therapy. March/April 2007 Volume 61, 2. Nieuwenhuys R. The Insular Cortex: A Review. Prog Brain Res. 2012; 195:123–63. doi: 10.1016/B978-0-444-53860-4.00007-6. Review. PMID:

O'Brien, Christine, 2014 http://www.teacherspayteachers.com/Store/Christine-Obrien

Ogino, Y., Nemoto, H., Inui, K., Saito, S., Kakigi, R., & Goto, F. (2007). Inner experience of pain: Imagination of pain while viewing images showing painful events forms subjective pain representation in human brain. *Cerebral Cortex*, 17, 1139–1146.

Olausson, H., Charron, J., Marchand, S., Villemure, C., Strigo, I. A., Bushnell, M. C. (2005). Feelings of warmth correlate with neural activity in right anterior insular cortex. *Neuroscience Letters* 25, 389, 1–5.

Oppenheimer, S. M., Gelb, A., Girvin, J. P., & Hachinski, V. C. (1992). Cardiovascular effects of human insular cortex stimulation. *Neurology*, 42, 1727–1732.

Ortigue, S., Grafton, S. T. & Bianchi-Demicheli, F. (2007). Correlation between insula activation and self-reported quality of orgasm in women. *Neuroimage*, 37, 551–560.

Paulus, M. P., (2005). Neurobiology of decision-making: quo vadis? *Cognitive Brain Research*, 23, 2–10. Penfield, W. & Faulk, M. E. (1955). The insula. *Brain*, 78, 445–470.

Paulus, M. P., Feinstein, J. S., Castillo, G., Simmons, A. N., & Stein, M. B. (2005). Dose-dependent decrease of activation in bilateral amygdale and insula by lorazepam during emotion processing. *Archives of General Psychiatry*, 62, 282–288.

Paulus, M. P., Rogalsky, C., Simmons, A., Feinstein, J. S., & Stein, M. B., (2003). Increased activation in the right insula during risk-taking decision making is related to harm avoidance and neuroticism. *NeuroImage*, 19, 1439–1448.

Paulus, M. P. & Stein, M. B. (2006). An insular view of anxiety. *Biological Psychiatry*, 60, 383–387.

Phan, K. L., Wager, T., Taylor, S. F., & Liberzon, I. (2002). Functional neuroanatomy of emotion: A meta-analysis of emotion activation studies in PET and fMRI. Neuroimage, 16, 331–348.

Phillips, M. L., Young, A. W., Scott, S. K., Calder, A. J., Andrew, C., Giampietro, V. S., et al., (1998). Neural responses to facial and vocal expressions of fear and disgust. Proceedings of the Royal Society: Biological Sciences, 265, 1809–1817.

Phillips, M.L., Williams, L.M., Heining, M., Herba, C.M., Russell, T., Andrew, C., et al., (2004). Differential neural responses to overt and covert presentations of facial expressions of fear and disgust. NeuroImage, 21, 1484–1496.

Preuschoff, K., Quartz, S. R., Bossaerts, P., (2008). Human insula activation reflects risk prediction errors as well as risk. Journal of Neuroscience, 28, 2745–2752.

Purves D, Augustine GJ, Fitzpatrick D, et al., editors. Neuroscience. 2nd edition. Sunderland (MA): Sinauer Associates; 2001. The Olfactory Bulb. Available from: https://www.ncbi.nlm.nih.gov/books/NBK11158/

Ramautar, J. R., Slagter, H. A., Kok, A. & Ridderinkhof, K. R. (2006). Probability effects in the stop-signal paradigm: The insula and the significance of failed inhibition. Brain Research, 1105, 143–154.

Rolls, E. T., McCabe, C., Redoute, J., (2008). Expected value, reward outcome, and temporal difference error representations in a probabilistic decision task. Cerebral Cortex, 18, 652–663.

Romantshik O., Porter, R. H., Tillmann, V., Varendi, H. (2007). Preliminary evidence of a sensitive period for olfactory learning by human newborns. 2007; 96: 372–376.

Sanfey, A. G., Rilling, J. K., Aronson, J. A., Nystrom, L. E., & Cohen, J. D. (2003). The neural basis of economic decision-making in the Ultimate Game. Science, 300, 1755–1758.

Seymour, B., Singer, T., & Dolan, R. (2007). The neurobiology of punishment. Nature Reviews Neuroscience, 8, 300–311.

Should I Go With My Gut? Investigating the Benefits of Emotion-Focused Decision Making (PDF Download Available).https://www.researchgate.net/publication/51189959_Should_I_Go_With_My_Gut_Investigating_the_Benefits_of_Emotion-Focused_Decision_Making [accessed Feb 18 2018].

Siegel, D. J., Bryson, T. P., (2015). The Whole-Brain Child Workbook. PESI Publishing and Media.

Small, D. M., Zatorre, R. J., Dagher, A., Evans, A. C. & Jones-Gotman, M. (2001). Changes in brain activity related to eating chocolate: from pleasure to aversion. Brain, 124, 1720–1733.

Smith, B. W., Mitchell, D. G. V., Hardin, M. G., Jazbec, S., Fridberg, D., Blair, R. J. R., & Ernst, M. (2009). Neural substrates of reward magnitude, probability, and risk during a wheel of fortune decision-making task. NeuroImage, 44, 600–609.

Stephani, C., Fernandez-Baca Vaca, G., Maciunas, R., Koubeissi, M., & Lüders, H. O. (2011). Functional neuroanatomy of the insular lobe. *Brain Structure & Function*, *216*(2), 137–149. http://doi.org/10.1007/s00429-010-0296-3

Stein, M. B., Simmons, A. N., Feinstein, J. S., & Paulhus, M. P. (2007). Increased amygdala and insula activation during emotion processing in anxiety-prone subjects. American Journal of Psychiatry, 164, 318–327.

Sze JA, Gyurak A, Yuan JW, Levenson RW (2010) Coherence between emotional experience and physiology: does body awareness training have an impact? Emotion 10: 803–814. doi: 10.1037/a0020146

Taylor, K. S., Seminowicz, D. A. and Davis, K. D. (2009), Two systems of resting state connectivity between the insula and cingulate cortex. Hum. Brain Mapp., 30: 2731–2745. doi:10.1002/hbm.20705

Thayer, J. F., & Lane, R. D. (2000). A model of neurovisceral integration in emotion regulation and dysregulation. Journal of Affective Disorders, 61, 201–216.

Therapeutic Touch Evidence-Based Therapy http://therapeutictouch.org/

Trivedi, M. H. (2004). The Link Between Depression and Physical Symptoms. *Primary Care Companion to The Journal of Clinical Psychiatry*, *6*(suppl 1), 12–16.

Tsakiris, M., Hesse, M. D., Boy, C., Haggard, P., & Fink, G. R. (2007). Neural signatures of body ownership: a sensory network for bodily self-consciousness. Cerebral Cortex, 17, 2235–2244.

Van Rooij, D,. Anagnostu, E., Arango, C., Auzias, G., Behrmann, M., Busatto, G. F., Calderoni, S., Daly, E., Deruelle, C., DiMartino., A., Dinstein, I., Duran, F. L. S., Durston S., Ecker, C., Gori, I., Fedor, J., Fitzgerals, J., Freitag, C. M., Gallagher, L., Gori, I., Haar, S., Hoekstra, L., Jananshad, N., Jalbrzikowski, M., Janssen, J., Lerch, J., Luna, B., Martinho, M.M., McGrath, J., Muratori, F., Murphy, C.M., Murphy, D.G. M., O'Hern, K., Oranje, B., Parallada, M., Retico, A., Rossa, P., Rubia., K. Shook, D., Taylor, M, Thompson, P. M., Tosetti, M., Wallace, G.K., Zhou, F., Buitelaar, J.K., (2017). Cortical and Subcortical Brain Morphometry Differences Between Patients With Autism Spectrum Disorder and Healthy Individuals Across the Lifespan: Results From the ENIGMA ASD Working Group. American Journal of Psychiatry, ahead of print https://ajp.psychiatryonline.org/doi/10.1176/appi.ajp.2017.17010100

Vermetten E & Bremner JD. Olfaction as a traumatic reminder in posttraumatic stress disorder: case reports and review. The Journal of Clinical Psychiatry 64 (2003), 202–207.

Vorel, S. R., Bisaga, A., McKhann, G., & Kleber, H. D. (2007). Insula damage and quitting smoking. *Science*, 317, 318–319.

Wicker, B., Keysers, C., Plailly, J., Royet, J. P., Gallese, V., & Rizzolatti, G. (2003). Both of us disgusted in My insula: The common neural basis of seeing and feeling disgust, Neuron, 40, 655–656.

Wilbarger, J. & Wilbarger, P. (2002). Wilbarger approach to treating sensory defensiveness and clinical application of the sensory diet. Sections in alternative and complementary programs for intervention, In Bundy, A.C., Murray, E.A., & Lane, S. (Eds.). *Sensory Integration: Theory and Practice*, 2nd Ed. F.A. Davis, Philadelphia, PA.

Williams, M.S., & Shellenberger, S. (1996). How does your engine run? A leader's guide to the Alert Program for self-regulation. Albuquerque, NM: Therapy Works, INC.

Williamson, J. W., McColl, R., Mathews, D., Ginsburg, M., & Mitchell, J. H. (1999). Activation of the insular cortex is affected by the intensity of exercise. *Journal of Applied Physiology*, 87, 1213–1219.

Wright, P., He, G., Shapira, N. A., Goodman, W. K., & Liu, Y. (2004). Disgust and the insula: fMRI responses to pictures of mutilation and contamination. Neuroreport, 15, 2347–2351.

Wright, P., Martin, B., McMullin, K., Sin, L. M., & Rauch, S. L. (2003). Amygdala and insular responses to emotionally valenced human faces in small animal specific phobia. Biological Psychiatry, 54, 1067–1076.

Yasuyuki Futagi, Yasuhisa Toribe, and Yasuhiro Suzuki, "The Grasp Reflex and Moro Reflex in Infants: Hierarchy of Primitive Reflex Responses," International Journal of Pediatrics, vol. 2012, Article ID 191562, 10 pages, 2012. doi:10.1155/2012/191562

Younger Chiropractic Clinic. (March 21, 2017). The Effects of Stress and Anxiety on Your Body. accessed 1/23/18 https://www.youngerchiropractic. co.uk/effects-of-stress-and-anxiety-on-your-body

ACTIVITY SHEET DOWNLOADS

Visit

https://www.pocketot.com/
interoceptionbook

to download your Activity Sheet packet.

Made in the USA
Columbia, SC
19 October 2023

24609328R00102